ADVANCED QFD APPLICATIONS

Also available from ASQ Quality Press:

Customer Driven Healthcare: QFD for Process Improvement and Cost Reduction
Ed Chaplin and John Terninko

Improving Your Measurement of Customer Satisfaction: A Guide to Creating, Conducting, Analyzing, and Reporting Customer Satisfaction Measurement Programs
Terry G. Vavra

Developing New Services: Incorporating the Voice of the Customer into Strategic Service Development
Caroline Fisher and James Schutta

Principles and Practices of Organizational Performance Excellence
Thomas J. Cartin

Quality Function Deployment: Linking a Company with Its Customers
Ronald G. Day

Breaking the Constraints to World-Class Performance
H. William Dettmer

Goldratt's Theory of Constraints: A Systems Approach to Continuous Improvement
H. William Dettmer

To request a complimentary catalog of ASQ Quality Press publications, call 800-248-1946, or visit our Web site at http://qualitypress.asq.org.

ADVANCED QFD
APPLICATIONS

Min Xie, Kay-Chuan Tan, and
Thong Ngee Goh

ASQ Quality Press
Milwaukee, Wisconsin

American Society for Quality, Quality Press, Milwaukee 53203

© 2003 by ASQ

12 11 10 09 08 07 06 05 04 03   5 4 3 2 1

Library of Congress Cataloging-in-Publication Data

Xie, M. (Min)
    Advanced QFD applications / by Min Xie, Kay-Chuan Tan, and Thong Ngee Goh.
    p. cm.

Includes bibliographical references and index.
    ISBN 0-87389-586-X
    1. Quality function deployment. I. Goh, T. N. (Thong Ngee) II. Tan,
    K. C. III. Title.

    TS156.X52 2003
    658.5'62--dc21

                                    2003005125
    ISBN 0-87389-586-X

Publisher: William A. Tony
Acquisitions Editor: Annemieke Koudstaal
Project Editor: Paul O'Mara
Production Administrator: Gretchen Trautman
Special Marketing Representative: Robin Barry

ASQ Mission: The American Society for Quality advances individual, organizational, and community excellence worldwide through learning, quality improvement, and knowledge exchange.

Attention Bookstores, Wholesalers, Schools and Corporations: ASQ Quality Press books, videotapes, audiotapes, and software are available at quantity discounts with bulk purchases for business, educational, or instructional use. For information, please contact ASQ Quality Press at 800-248-1946, or write to ASQ Quality Press, P.O. Box 3005, Milwaukee, WI 53201-3005.

To place orders or to request a free copy of the ASQ Quality Press Publications Catalog, including ASQ membership information, call 800-248-1946. Visit our Web site at www.asq.org or http://qualitypress.asq.org.

 Printed on acid-free paper

American Society for Quality

ASQ

Quality Press
600 N. Plankinton Avenue
Milwaukee, Wisconsin 53203
Call toll free 800-248-1946
Fax 414-272-1734
www.asq.org
http://qualitypress.asq.org
http://standardsgroup.asq.org
E-mail: authors@asq.org

Table of Contents

Preface

Quality is probably the most important selling point today. Higher quality eventually leads to a larger market share, a higher selling price, or both, thus higher profit. Quality engineering aims at analyzing products and processes to reduce production cost and improve customer satisfaction. It is important to study the tools that can be used for these purposes.

Quality function deployment (QFD) is a widely–used tool in both quality management and quality engineering. QFD helps to translate customer needs and requirements into product and process design characteristics so that they can be best designed to improve customer satisfaction. However, most of the existing literature on QFD deals mainly with the basic QFD applications and their general benefits. An integral part of QFD, the house of quality (HOQ), for example, is generally not analyzed beyond its basic formulation.

The aim of this book is to take some steps beyond the basic QFD analysis to maximize its potential in practical applications. The emphasis is on both quantitative and qualitative analyses. A number of techniques for further analysis of the HOQ are described and illustrated with simple examples. Although we hope that the readers will have some basic idea of QFD in order to read and use this book, no in-depth knowledge or experience with QFD is required.

A general discussion is presented in Chapter 1 to provide some historical background of QFD. Chapter 2 contains a basic introduction to QFD that is suitable for beginners. An application example is presented. In this chapter, a summary of some current studies of advanced QFD analysis is also provided.

Chapters 3 through 5 deal with several important issues that are usually not found in standard QFD texts. Chapter 3 focuses on the prediction of the voice of the customer, especially their future voices. Some methods for this type of analysis and use of the voice of the customer are discussed. Chapter 4 deals with some quantitative analysis on handling variability in gathering customers' voices. Sensitivity analysis of the QFD processes is also discussed. Some detailed optimization models that make use of HOQ are discussed in Chapter 5. The aim in this chapter is to provide some techniques for detailed analysis and optimization for better resource allocation and decision making.

Chapters 6 through 8 present some detailed analysis on the use of benchmarking data and information, Kano's model for better customer satisfaction, and QFD for service-related applications. The discussion here provides more insights into QFD applications with a focus on the spoken and unspoken customer needs. Finally, in Chapter 9, we summarize some other advanced QFD applications for cases where there are segmented customer groups and linguistic data. We also present a study on the reduction of the HOQ for better presentation and decision making.

Many illustrative examples from service, the Internet, product design, and so on are shown in this book together with advanced and further analyses in QFD. This self-contained book can be used as a reference text for basic quality or management courses, or as a main text for senior or graduate-level courses on QFD. It can also be used for training or self-study.

This is a unique and useful book, much different from many existing QFD books on the market. We hope that this book will serve as a valuable addition to the quality literature. Furthermore, it is the aim of this book to bring together QFD practitioners and researchers to make the QFD even more useful for quality professionals and decision makers.

We would like to thank a number of individuals who have helped in the process of preparing this book. First of all, the contribution of many of our students, especially Dr. H. Wang, Dr. X. X. Shen, Mr. K. L. Sim, Ms. R. Vijayalakshmi, and Ms. T. Pawitra are acknowledged. Their interest and hard work have motivated us to finally complete this book. The support and interest of many of our colleagues are also acknowledged.

The help of Mr. Michael O'Donoghue of the American Society for Quality in getting this project started is very much appreciated. The book was initiated after his visit to Singapore Quality Institute, with which we are associated. We also appreciate the help of Ms. Annemieke Koudstaal and Mr. Paul O'Mara of the ASQ Quality Press, as well as several reviewers who have provided many useful comments to earlier versions of the manuscript.

Finally, we would like to thank our families for their support and understanding through the course of research and preparation for this book.

Min Xie
Kay-Chuan Tan
Thong Ngee Goh

Singapore, 1 February 2003

Chapter 1
Introduction

Product quality is probably the most vital selling point in today's global market. For improvement of quality and productivity, many companies have adopted total quality management (TQM) as a key initiative with the use of methods, such as quality function deployment (QFD), design for manufacturability, and statistical process control. Among these approaches, QFD has been used to translate customer needs into engineering design characteristics through the integration of marketing, design, engineering, manufacturing, and other relevant functions of an organization (Akao, 1990; Cohen, 1995).

QFD could enable a company to improve its products and processes to levels exceeding the expectation of the customer. It works best within a company when there are organizational commitment and a disciplined approach to implementation. The QFD discipline provides both a framework and a structured process to enhance an organization's ability to communicate, document, analyze, and prioritize. The documentation and analysis steps lead to breakthroughs that enhance competitiveness.

DEFINITION AND USES OF QFD

The term *quality function deployment* originated from a Japanese phrase consisting of three characters with the following meanings:

— *Hin shitsu*, which can mean "quality," "features," "attributes," or "qualities"

— *Kin*, which can mean "functions" or "mechanisms"

—*Ten kai*, which can mean "deployment," "evolution," "diffusion," or "development"

According to the translation of these Japanese phrases, QFD means deploying the attributes of a product or service desired by the customer throughout all the appropriate functional components of an organization (ReVelle et al., 1998). QFD also provides a mechanism for its achievement, that is, the set of matrices that serves as both a structure and a graphic of the deployment process. However, there are several different definitions that have been proposed in the literature.

According to Akao (1990), QFD is defined as "a method for developing a design quality aimed at satisfying the consumer and translating the consumer's demand into design targets and major quality assurance points to be used throughout the production phase." Sullivan (1986) conceptualized QFD as "a method that helps a manufacturing company to bring new products to the market sooner than competition with lower cost and improved quality."

Quality function deployment, according to the American Supplier Institute (ASI), is defined as "A system for translating customer or user requirements into appropriate company requirements at every stage from research, through product design and development, to manufacture, distribution, installation and marketing, sales, and service."

According to Growth Opportunity Alliance of Lawrence, Massachusetts/ Quality Productivity Center (GOAL/QPC), QFD is a system for designing products and services based on customer demand and involving all members of the producer or supplier organizations. It is sometimes referred to as the most advanced form of total quality control, Japanese style.

QFD is a way of making the voice of the customer heard throughout an organization. It is a systematic process for capturing customer requirements and translating them into requirements that must be met throughout the supply chain (Hutton, 2001). The result is a set of target values for designers, production people, and even suppliers to aim at, in order to produce the output desired by the customer.

QFD is particularly valuable when design trade-offs are necessary in order to achieve the best overall solution, for example, when some requirements conflict with others. QFD also enables a great deal of information to be summarized in the form of one or more charts.

QFD is sometimes referred to by other names, such as *the voice of the customer* (VOC) (from its use as a way of communicating customer needs) or *the house of quality* (HOQ) (from the characteristic house shape of a QFD chart, see Figure 1.1).

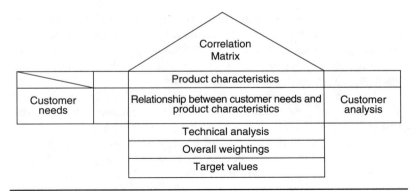

Figure 1.1   The house of quality is the basic matrix structure used to define the voice of the customer.

Benefits of QFD

QFD is not simply a tool. It can be seen as an entire quality system (Govers, 2001); it can also be seen as a planning process (Day, 1993), a mechanism (Sullivan, 1986), and a methodology. Since its first use, QFD has been accepted by a large number of organizations worldwide, for example, Du Pont, General Motors, IBM, AT&T, Digital, Motorola, Philips International, and Texas Instruments (Burn, 1990; Kathawala and Motwani, 1994; Chan and Wu, 2002).

To a large extent, the widespread acceptance of QFD is due to many of its benefits. The power of QFD lies in its exposing an organization's processes and showing how these processes interact to create customer satisfaction and profit (Raynor, 1994). QFD users claim and often report benefits, such as the following:

- Reduced design cycle time and engineering changes

- Minimized start-up costs

- Tremendous efficiency, including shorter lead times

- Reduction in prelaunch time and after-launch tinkering

- Increased customer satisfaction and market share

- Reduced warranty claims

- More stable quality assurance planning

- Fewer product returns

In addition to the above arguments, other benefits of QFD include superior product design, the potential for breakthrough innovation, and low project and product costs. QFD also helps companies discover that innovation, manufacturing, and quality can fit together comfortably. Kenny (1988) argued that QFD is a new paradigm for quality assurance. QFD can be viewed as one of the main pillars for successful *total quality management* and *product development* (Zairi and Youssef, 1995). More discussion can be found in Burke et al. (2003) in which some misuses are also discussed.

The uses of QFD are not limited to improving an existing product. QFD is also useful in new product design, as the focus on QFD analysis is to address the needs of customers. Furthermore, QFD is useful in both product design and process design. In addition, since QFD requires an organizational effort, teamwork is promoted; this is very important for complex products and processes.

In investigating the impact of QFD on product development, numerous field studies and surveys have been conducted. One of the assumptions when working with QFD is that a *cross-functional team* carries out the project. This is in order to use the experience of people with different backgrounds and to cut through the functional barriers. Based on a field comparison of QFD and the phase-review product development process, Griffin and Hauser (1993) concluded that this new pattern of communication appears to increase team communication on all nonadministrative aspects of new product development. An empirical study of QFD's impact on product development was carried out recently. Vonderembse et al. (1997) and Vonderembse and Raghunathan (1997) investigated the technical, organizational, and personal dimensions of QFD that lead to its successful application. Based on a survey of 80 QFD projects from 40 companies, they concluded that product design, documentation efforts, and customer satisfaction improved significantly. Product costs and time-to-market showed only modest improvement but may be bettered with enhanced training and more experience.

DEVELOPMENT OF QFD

Quality function deployment was originally developed in Japan as an effort to get engineers to consider quality early in the design process, and the idea was introduced in the 1960s to Japanese companies (Akao and Mazur 2003). Similar ideas were used in the Kobe shipyards of Mitsubishi Heavy Industries around 1972 (Shillito, 1994) as a way to expand and implement the views of quality as taught by Deming and others. The quality chart introduced later became known as the quality function deployment methodology.

Since then, it was developed further by the Japanese automotive industry. Toyota, in particular, used it to significantly reduce development time and to deal with more complex situations, as evidenced by their solutions to the serious problem of car body rust confronting Toyota cars. Car body rust was a common problem with Japanese cars in the 1960s and 1970s. Toyota made many attempts at improvement, but a real breakthrough eluded them. The seriousness of the problem was such that warranty charges exceeded company profit by a factor of four.

Body rust was a complex problem with many contributing factors (Burn, 1994). Toyota adopted the QFD process to identify and target the more important contributing factors, thus resulting in the elimination of body rust during the warranty period. The application of QFD has been one of the keys to Toyota's success.

QFD was formally introduced to the United States in 1983 by Furukawa, Kogure, and Akao during a four-day seminar for about 80 quality assurance managers from prominent U.S. companies. Also instrumental in the introduction of QFD in the United States was an article by Kogure and Akao in the October 1983 issue of *Quality Progress*: "Quality Function Deployment and CWQC in Japan" (ReVelle et al., 1997).

Because of the success of their Japanese competitors (especially Toyota), American companies started to investigate how the Japanese companies operated, thereby learning about QFD. In 1984, Donald Clausing introduced QFD to Ford. Eventually, enough was learned by some of the automotive-related training organizations that QFD started to be taught widely within the United States. Use of QFD has since spread into many nonautomotive industries.

Various QFD-related activities are currently carried out for its advancement. For example, an annual North American Symposium on QFD has been held in Novi, Michigan, starting in 1989. With the international trend in QFD development, the International Symposium on Quality Function Deployment (ISQFD) has also been held annually since 1995. Further, to provide a unified body to coordinate QFD organizations, efforts, and events around the world and to promote QFD-related research, the International Council for QFD (ICQFD) was established in 1997.

QFD APPLICATIONS

Since its introduction, QFD has been applied considerably in Japan. A survey of the Japanese Union of Scientists and Engineers member companies in 1986, for example, reported that 54 percent utilize QFD, with a majority in the high technology and transportation industries (Sullivan, 1986).

The QFD concept did not, however, appear in the English-language literature until 1983. With the widespread applications of QFD in Japan and the United States, it was also brought to the attention of companies in many other countries. This has led to a wide-spread application in terms of application areas and also in terms of functional stages of QFD process.

The traditional QFD model is based on the paradigm of designing and manufacturing physical objects, that is, hardware. However, QFD has been extended beyond its initial concept. It was reported that QFD has been applied to many other fields for various purposes. Some of the application areas include the following:

- Automotive (De Vera et al., 1988; Dika, 1995; Tsuda, 1997)

- Construction (Mallon and Mulligan, 1993; Armacost et al., 1994; Abdul-Rahman et al., 1999)

- Education (Chen and Bullington, 1993; Ermer, 1995, Pitman et al., 1995; Lam and Zhao, 1998; Franceschini and Terzago, 1998; Hwarng and Teo, 2001; Bier and Cornesky, 2001)

- Electronics (Burrows, 1991; Liner et al., 1997; Tan and Neo, 2002; Herzwurm and Schockert, 2003)

- Food industry (Charteris, 1993; Bech et al., 1997; Viaene and Januszewska, 1999; Costa et al., 2000)

- Healthcare (Hauser, 1993; Radharamanan and Godoy, 1996; Jeong and Oh, 1998; Foster, 2001)

- Marketing (Lu et al., 1994; Lu and Kuei, 1995; Mohr-Hackson, 1996; Vairaktarakis, 1999)

- Research and Development (Griffin, 1992; Tottie and Lager, 1995; Price, 1995; Matzler and Hinterhuber, 1998; Cristiano et al., 2000; Delano et al., 2000; Yamashina et al., 2002; Masui et al., 2003)

- Service (Denton, 1990; Graessel and Zeidler, 1993; Ghobadian and Terry, 1995; Ermer and Kniper, 1998; Dube et al., 1999; Pun et al., 2000; Selen and Schepers, 2001)

- Software (Zultner, 1990; Yoshizawa et al., 1993; Erikkson and McFadden, 1993; Barnett and Raja, 1995; Haag et al., 1996; Trappey et al., 1996; Elboushi and Sherif, 1997; Karlsson, 1997; Pai, 2002)

The above is only a list of selected papers. An extensive survey of the literature of quality function deployment is presented in Chan and Wu

(2002). Over 600 publications can be found in that paper. The classification is based on the functional fields of quality function deployment, as well as the applied industries.

SCOPE AND OBJECTIVES

The scope of this book includes a brief introduction to QFD, starting with its definition and a brief history. A review of QFD is presented next, which includes the various approaches to QFD, examples of its applications, some updates and observations, and the limitations of QFD. This book focuses on the voice of the customer, that is, the task of analyzing the importance ranking of customer needs, weighting scale of the relationship matrix, and the prioritization techniques. Examples are used and presented to help the reader to better understand the techniques and applications of QFD.

Chapter 2
QFD Basics

As ReVelle et al. (1997) explained, the need for QFD was driven by objectives that start with the customers of a product and end with its producers. Producers convert the customers' needs for product benefits into substitute quality characteristics at the design stage. They then deploy the substitute quality characteristics in the production activities, thereby establishing the necessary control points prior to production start-up.

This chapter presents the basic steps of QFD and the structure of the HOQ. Readers familiar with quality function deployment may skip this chapter and move on to Chapter 3. For more details on basic QFD and the implementation issues, Day (1993), Cohen (1995), ReVelle et al. (1997), and Chan and Wu (2003) are some useful references.

HOUSE OF QUALITY

The HOQ, sometimes also called the A-1 matrix, is the most commonly used matrix in the QFD methodology. The foundation of an HOQ is the belief that products should be designed to reflect customers' desires and tastes. Thus, marketing people, design engineers, and the manufacturing staff must work closely together from the time of product conceptualization. The HOQ is a kind of conceptual map that provides a means for inter-functional planning and communication (Hauser and Clausing, 1988).

The focus in HOQ is the correlation between the identified customer needs, called the *WHATs*, and the engineering characteristics, called *HOWs*. Ideally, an HOQ should be developed by a cross-functional team made up of members from various departments. It should consist of several submatrices joined together in various ways, each containing some information related to the others.

Structure of the House of Quality

The structure of QFD takes the shape of a house, which follows from the name *house of quality*. Its structure is shown in Figure 2.1. The parts of the HOQ are described as follows:

- The exterior walls of the house are the descriptions of customer requirements and expectations. On the left side is a listing of customer requirements. On the right side are the prioritized customer requirements, which reflect the importance of these expectations. Listed are items, such as competitive benchmarking, customer importance rating, target value, scale-up factor, and sales point.

- The ceiling of the house lists the engineering characteristics, sometimes also called technical descriptors or design characteristics. The technical descriptors of the product are provided through engineering requirements, design constraints, and parameters.

- The interior or living room of the house holds the relationships between customer requirements and engineering characteristics.

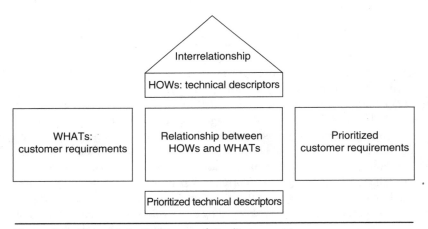

Figure 2.1   Elements in the House of Quality.

Customer expectations or requirements are translated into engineering characteristics through the relationships here.

- The roof of the house contains the interrelationships between engineering characteristics. Trade-offs between similar and/or conflicting engineering characteristics are contained here.

- At the foundation of the house lie the prioritized engineering characteristics. Factors such as technical benchmarking, degree of technical difficulty, and target values are listed.

QFD Process

Two popular models illustrate the QFD process. One is the four-phase model developed by Hauser and Clausing (1988). This is probably the most widely described and used. The other is by Dr. Akao (1990) called the "Matrix of Matrices." Akao's model is considered gigantic and far reaching (Cohen, 1995). The QFD structure is normally presented as a system of matrices, charts, tables, or other diagrams. Because the four-phase model seems to be more common in the English-language literature, we briefly describe it here (Figure 2.2).

The four-phase model is based on the following key documents or components (Sullivan, 1986):

1. Overall customer requirement planning matrix—*translates the general customer requirements into specified final product control characteristics.*

2. Final product characteristic development matrix—*translates the output of the planning matrix into critical component characteristics.*

3. Process plan and quality control charts—*identify critical product and process parameters and develop checkpoints and controls for these parameters.*

4. Operating instructions—*identify operations to be performed by plant personnel to ensure that important parameters are achieved.*

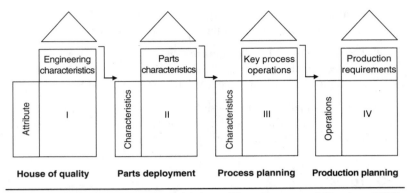

Figure 2.2 Four-phase QFD model (adapted from Hauser and Clausing, 1988).

CONSTRUCTION OF THE HOUSE OF QUALITY

The steps for the construction of the house of quality can be described as follows:

Step 1—List Customer Requirements (WHATs)

QFD starts with a list of goals/objectives. This list is often referred to as the WHATs that a customer needs or expects from a particular product. This list of primary customer requirements is usually vague and very general in nature. Further definition is accomplished by defining a new, more detailed list of secondary customer requirements to support the primary customer requirements. In other words, a primary customer requirement may encompass numerous secondary customer requirements. Although the items on the list of secondary customer requirements represent greater details than those on the list of primary customer requirements, they are often not directly actionable by the engineering staff and require further definition. Finally, the list of customer requirements is divided into a hierarchy of primary, secondary, and tertiary customer requirements, as shown in Table 2.1.

Step 2—List Engineering Characteristics (HOWs)

The goal of the HOQ is to design or change the design of a product in a way that meets or exceeds customer expectations. Now that customer needs and expectations have been expressed in terms of customer requirements, the QFD team must come up with the *engineering characteristics* that will affect one or more of the customer requirements. These engineering characteristics make

Table 2.1 Refinement of customer requirements.

	Customer requirements (WHATs)													
Primary														
Secondary														
Tertiary														

up the ceiling or second floor of the HOQ. Each engineering characteristic must directly affect a customer requirement and be expressed in measurable terms.

Implementation of customer requirements is difficult until they are translated into specific engineering characteristics. These characteristics are expressions of VOC in a technical language. Each of the customer requirements is broken down into the next level of detail by way of listing one or more primary engineering characteristics for each of the tertiary customer requirements. This process is similar to refining marketing specifications into system-level engineering specifications. Further definition of the primary engineering characteristics is accomplished by defining a list of secondary engineering characteristics that represent greater details than those on the list of primary engineering characteristics. These secondary engineering characteristics can include part specifications and manufacturing parameters that an engineer can act upon.

Often the secondary engineering characteristics are still not directly actionable, requiring yet further definition. This process of refinement is continued until every item on the list is actionable. Finally, the list of engineering characteristics is divided into a hierarchy of primary, secondary, and tertiary engineering characteristics. The structure is similar to the refinement of customer requirements shown in Table 2.1.

Step 3—Develop a Relationship Matrix Between the WHATs and the HOWs

The next step in building an HOQ is to compare customer requirements and engineering characteristics, and to determine their respective relationships. The task of tracing the relationships between the customer requirements and the engineering characteristics can become very complex, because each customer requirement may affect more than one engineering characteristic, and vice versa.

The inside of the HOQ, called the *relationship matrix,* is now filled in by the QFD team. The relationship matrix is used to represent graphically the degree of influence between each engineering characteristic and each customer requirement. This step may take a long time, because the number of evaluations is the product of the number of customer requirements and the number of engineering characteristics. Doing this early in the development process will shorten the development cycle and should lessen the need for future changes.

It is common to use symbols to represent the degrees of relationships between the customer requirements and engineering characteristics. For example, the following system can be adopted:

A dark circle (●) represents a strong relationship.

A single circle (○) represents a medium relationship.

A triangle (∇) represents a weak relationship.

The box is left blank if no relationship exists.

During the quantitative analysis of the importance weights of the engineering characteristics, the symbols that are used to define the relationships are replaced with numbers, for example:

Strong relationship = 5 (or 9)

Medium relationship = 3

Weak relationship = 1

The above weights can be used later in determining the absolute weights of the engineering characteristics. These are located at the bottom of the matrix.

In the relationship matrix, an empty row indicates that a customer requirement is not being addressed by any of the engineering characteristics. Thus, the customer expectation is not being met. Additional engineering characteristics or process changes must be considered in order to satisfy that particular customer requirement. An empty column indicates that a particular engineering characteristic does not affect any of the customer requirements and, after careful scrutiny, may be removed from the HOQ.

Step 4—Develop an Interrelationship Matrix Between Pairs of HOWs

The roof of the HOQ, called the correlation matrix, is used to identify any interrelationships between pairs of engineering characteristics. It is a triangular table attached to the engineering characteristics. Symbols are used to describe the strength of the interrelationships. For example, similar to the case of the relationship matrix, the following system can be used:

A dark circle (●) represents a strong positive relationship.

A single circle (○) represents a positive relationship.

A single X represents a negative relationship.

A double XX represents a strong negative relationship.

The correlation matrix allows the user to identify which engineering characteristics are most important because they are frequently the result of conflicting customer requirements and, consequently, represent points at which trade-offs must be made. Trade-offs that are not identified and resolved will often lead to unfulfilled requirements, engineering changes, increased costs, and poorer quality. Some of the trade-offs may require high-level managerial decisions, because they are cross-functional area boundaries. Even though it is difficult, early resolution of trade-offs is essential to shorten product development time.

It should be pointed out that in some other places the interrelationships are simplified to have only two kinds of relationships, namely: negative and positive relationships. A symbol "+" is often used for synergy and a "−" is used for compromise.

Step 5—Competitive Assessments

The competitive assessments are a pair of weighted tables that compare the performance of the current organization's products in their key specifications with those of their competitors. The competitive assessment tables are separated into two categories, customer assessment and technical assessment.

1. *Customer Competitive Assessment.* The customer competitive assessment makes up a block of columns corresponding to each customer requirement in the HOQ on the right side of the relationship matrix. The numbers 1 through 5 are listed in the competitive evaluation column with a rating of 1 assigned to the worst competitor, while a 5 is assigned to the best competitor. These rankings can also be plotted across from each customer requirement, using different symbols for each product.

The customer competitive assessment is a good way to determine if the customer requirements have been met, and to identify areas to concentrate on in the next design. The customer competitive assessment also contains an appraisal of where an organization stands relative to its major competitors in terms of each customer requirement. Both of these assessments are very important, because they give the organization an understanding of where its products stand in relationship to the market.

2. *Technical Competitive Assessment.* The technical competitive assessment makes up a block of rows corresponding to each engineering characteristic in the HOQ beneath the relationship matrix. After respective units have been established, the products are evaluated for each engineering characteristic. Similar to the customer competitive assessment, the test data are converted to numbers 1 through 5 which are listed in the competitive evaluation row to indicate a rating: 1 for the worst and 5 for the best. These rankings can then be plotted below each engineering characteristic using the same symbols used in the customer competitive assessment.

Step 6—Develop the Prioritized Customer Requirements

The prioritized customer requirements make up a block of columns corresponding to each customer requirement in the HOQ on the right-hand side of the relationship matrix. These prioritized customer requirements contain columns for importance to customers, target values, scale-up factors, sales points, and absolute weightings of the customer requirements.

1. *Importance rating.* The QFD team—or, preferably, the customer focus group—ranks each customer requirement by assigning it a rating. Numbers 1 through 10 are listed in the importance-to-customer column. Number 1 signifies the lowest importance rating; number 10 signifies the highest importance rating.

2. *Target value.* The target-value column is on the same scale as the customer competitive assessment. The following scale can be used: 1 for the worst, 5 for the best. This column is where the QFD team decides whether it wants to keep its product unchanged, improve the product, or make the product better than the competitors'.

3. *Scale-up factor.* The scale-up factor is the ratio of the target value to the product rating given in the customer competitive assessment. The higher the number, the more effort is needed. Here, the important consideration is the level the product is at now, what the target rating is, and deciding whether the difference is within reason. Sometimes there is not a choice because of difficulties in meeting the target. Consequently, the target ratings often need to be reduced to more realistic values.

4. *Sales point.* The sales point tells the QFD team how much it is estimated that satisfying this customer requirement will improve sales of the product. The objective here is to promote the best customer requirement and any remaining customer requirements that will help in the sale of the

product. For example, the sales point can be normalized to a value of 1.5 for the most saleable customer requirement.

5. *Absolute weight.* Finally, the absolute weight is calculated by multiplying the importance rating, scale-up factor, and sales point:

Absolute Weight = (Importance Rating) × (Scale-up Factor) × (Sales Point)

Step 7—Develop the Prioritized Engineering Characteristics

The prioritized engineering characteristics make up a block of rows at the bottom of the HOQ corresponding to each engineering characteristic in the HOQ. These prioritized engineering characteristics contain the degrees of technical difficulty, the target values, and absolute and relative weights. The QFD team identifies engineering characteristics that are most needed to fulfill customer requirements. These measures provide specific objectives that guide the subsequent design and provide a means of objectively assessing progress and minimizing subjective opinions.

1. *Degree of difficulty.* Many users of the HOQ add the degree of technical difficulty for implementing each engineering characteristic, which is expressed in the last row of the prioritized engineering characteristics. The degree of technical difficulty, when used, helps to evaluate the ability to implement certain engineering characteristics.

2. *Target value.* A target value is an objective measure that defines values that must be obtained in order to achieve the engineering characteristic. How much it takes to meet or exceed the customers' expectations is answered by evaluating all the information entered into the HOQ and selecting target values.

3. *Absolute weight.* The last two rows of the prioritized engineering characteristics are the absolute weights and relative weights. A popular and easy method for determining the weights is to assign numerical values to symbols in the relationship matrix.

The absolute weight of the jth engineering characteristic is thus given by

$$a_j = \sum_{i=1}^{n} R_{ij} c_i, j = 1, ..., m \qquad (2.1)$$

where R_{ij} = weights assigned to the relationship matrix ($i = 1, ..., n, j = 1, ..., m$)

c_i = column vector of degree of importance for the customer requirements ($i = 1, ..., n$)

m = number of engineering characteristics

n = number of customer requirements

Here a_j, which is called the row vector of absolute weights for the engineering characteristic j, can then be used and compared with that of other engineering characteristics. A percentage or relative importance can also be computed.

A QFD APPLICATION EXAMPLE

In this section, a detailed description of the method of QFD is presented via a case study (Sim, 2000). The case is the design of an Auto Compactor Bin (ACB), or automatic garbage compactor. The objective is to illustrate the steps of basic QFD and its applications. Readers already familiar with QFD may skip this section.

Capturing the Voice of the Customer

The first step is to generate a list of items representing the voice of the customer. This is completed through interviews and surveys. The customer needs are refined and grouped as shown in Figure 2.3.

The VOCs are also rated on a scale of 1 to 10. Ten represents very important, while 1 represents unimportant. Importance rating is critical in the QFD process because it serves as weighting factors. These customer-assigned weights then become multipliers for other numbers in the matrix, affecting subsequent statistical analyses, decisions, and conclusions.

Listing of Engineering Characteristics

The next task is to generate a list of engineering characteristics that must be measurable and meaningful to the designer. This part of the QFD process requires the use of collective knowledge of the design team. Brainstorming is usually needed.

Using team brainstorming and expertise, a list of product features or engineering characteristics is generated. These characteristics are arranged into a hierarchy using the tree diagram as shown in Figure 2.4.

Once the listing of the engineering characteristics is completed, appropriate characteristics are identified. As with the customer needs, engineering characteristics must be quantified. Therefore, the target goals for each engineering characteristic are determined and marked using one of the three symbols. Target goals are located above the engineering characteristics. An up arrow (↑) shows an increase, a down arrow (↓) shows a decrease, and a circle (○) signifies a fixed target value.

Primary	Secondary	Tertiary	Importance
Enhances product quality	Good appearance	Looks attractive	7
		Easy to clean	8
		No spillage during compacting	9
		Not too tall	4
		Not too bulky	5
		Able to blend with the ambient	6
		Noncorrosive material	4
	Safety and environment friendly	Safe to use	6
		Must not produce a lot of noise	3
		Has an emergency button	4
		Material used must be heat resistant	5
		Must not be distorted after compacting	8
		Must not give out foul smell	7
		No leakage	8
		Has indication during compacting process	7
		Auto locking of lid when compactor is in operation	6
		Must be rigid and firm	7
Good operation, and user friendly	Ease of operation	Easy to throw rubbish from outside	9
		Easy to empty a fully loaded bin	8
		Easy to open or close door	5
		Lid opening must be big enough	6
		Easy to operate	7
		Operational manual	2
		Ergonomically designed for all ages	6
		Fully automatic	3
		Able to move from one place to another	2
		Not too heavy	1
		Has side handles	3
		Incorporates shelves into the design	6
	Lower cost	Not too expensive	8
		Contains as much trash as possible	9
		Low maintenance cost	4
		Low energy consumption	5
		Not labor intensive to maintain	6

Figure 2.3   Refined group customer data.

To illustrate how the target goals are deployed in the ACB example, in order to "look attractive," the surface roughness of the frame must be improved. Thus, the target goal for the "surface roughness of the frame" would be to decrease its roughness.

Relating the Customer Needs to the Engineering Characteristics

For the next step, symbols are used to depict the relationship between the customer needs and the engineering characteristics (Table 2.2). This relationship matrix is located in the center of the HOQ.

Relationships are determined by asking the question "Will this engineering characteristic have an effect on satisfying the customers' needs?"

Primary	Secondary	Tertiary
Design factor and operating effort	Frame structure	Check surface roughness of the frame
		Outlook color of the frame structure
		Corrosion resistance of structure material
		Strength of the structure material
		Heat resistance of the structure material
		Overall structure size (w x d x h)
		Overall structure weight
		Handle dimension (diameter x length)
		Size of shelves (w x d x h)
		Label indicating operating procedure
		Time taken to clear rubbish
		Frequency of daily rubbish clearing
		Time taken to throw rubbish
	Compactor	Size of compactor plate (w x l x t)
		Noise level when compacting
		Meet required compacting force
	Lid and door	Size of lid opening (w x l)
		Spring force of lid opening (hinged)
		Position of lid opening from floor
		Energy to open/close the door
	Bin	Size of the bin (w x d x h)
		Meet waterproof test
		Weight of the bin
		Impact resistance of the bin
	Other standard component	Energy to drive the motor
		Capacity of PLC
		Power rating of LCD display
		LCD display test
		Capacity of torque limiter
		Number of emergency buttons
		Number of interlocking sensors
		Test sustaining force of the interlock bar

Figure 2.4   Engineering characteristics.

The design team would respond to each question and the responses are entered into the relationship matrix, using the symbols shown in Table 2.2.

For illustration, starting with the first customer need, the question is asked: Can "check surface roughness of the frame" help to achieve "looks attractive"? If the answer is "NO," enter a "0" or leave it blank in the relationship matrix. If the team responds with a "YES," then ask: Is the relationship low, medium, or high?

The team then proceeds down the column to the next customer need, and finishes off the column before proceeding to the next engineering characteristic. The completion of the relationship matrix is based purely on team experience when responding to each question. With these relationship matrices, there tends to be a better understanding of how one change of any

Table 2.2   Symbols used in relationship matrix.

Symbol	Score	
	0	No relationship
▽	1	Low or weak relationship
◯	3	Medium relationship
●	5	High or very strong relationship

engineering characteristic would affect the others. Trade-offs between characteristics can be assessed as well.

Calculating the Relationship Score of Engineering Characteristics

In the cells containing numerical relationships, each score (1, 3, or 5) is multiplied by the corresponding importance rating score for the customer need. In the ACB example, the cell representing "looks attractive" and "check surface roughness" contains a product of 7 × 5 = 35. Likewise, the other corresponding importance rating score multiplies the other relationship score under the column "check surface roughness."

The absolute score is then calculated by summing all the products in the column. For example, under the "Check surface roughness of the frame" column, (7 × 5) + (8 × 5) + (6 × 3) = 93. The column totals represent a rank order of engineering characteristics weighted by customer needs. For this case, a relative score of 9 was obtained, and is indicated in the relative score row. The result indicates how much influence the engineering characteristics have in meeting customer needs.

Deploying the Correlation Matrix

The correlation matrix takes the shape of a pitched roof and shows the positive and negative relationships among the engineering characteristics. It is used to determine which engineering characteristics support each other, and where conflicts can occur. Four symbols are normally used in the correlation matrix to indicate their relationships, as shown in Table 2.3.

Table 2.3 Symbols used in correlation matrix.

Symbol	Relationship
●	Strong positive
○	Medium positive
▽	Medium negative
▯	Strong negative

One begins by asking if there is a relationship between the pairs of engineering characteristics. Appropriate symbols are entered into the intersecting cell that depicts the relationships.

To illustrate its use, consider the ACB example again. Any change in the "size of the lid opening" will have little effect on any of the other engineering characteristics except for a strong positive relationship with "time taken to throw rubbish" and "overall structure size." This is ideal because the size of the lid opening is a high-scoring engineering characteristic, and has little interaction with other engineering characteristics. This makes it much easier to change the specification of this engineering characteristic.

Competitive Benchmarking and Further Analysis

This is another important step that allows priorities to be set in the design process, and can be done with the HOQ. It can be a difficult and challenging task, however, when there is no competitor with exactly the same product.

In the case of the ACB example, competitors offering products with similar functions are identified. Based on the team members' experiences, interviews, and feedback from others, such as friends and colleagues, the rating results were obtained. The evaluation of all competitor products with respect to the design is performed using a simple coding scheme shown in Table 2.4.

The results were compiled and indicated on the right-hand side of the HOQ. The dotted line traces the position of the design in relation to the competitor products. This permits the reader to get a good global overview of the performance of ACB against its competitors.

Table 2.4 Symbols for our product and competing products for customer perception analysis.

☺	Our Bin
♊	"A" Bin
⧗	"B" Bin

There are two parts to competitive benchmarking: (i) the process of competitive benchmarking, and (ii) the determination of objective target values. The former is similar to the customer competitive benchmarking but involves going into the technical details of the product. For the objective target values, engineering specifications are established.

The same competitors and products are used for competitive benchmarking. In keeping with the use of numeric conventions in the QFD process, we use the standard 1 through 5 scale, where 1 corresponds to weak performance and 5 corresponds to superior performance. Team members would use their experience to reach a consensus on a score for each engineering characteristic and each competitor. Their scores are displayed in a table located in the technical competitive benchmarking row.

Finally, the objective target values for the product are established. The team determines *how much* must be done to be competitive in the marketplace, and to what extent each engineering characteristic must be changed. Normally these values are created according to industry and company standards. But in this case, the standard is based on the evaluation of the customer wants and what the competition offers.

Now that the house is built, useful information can be obtained to achieve its design objectives. In the ACB example, since the "size of lid opening" was ranked first based on the absolute score, it has a high influence on meeting customer needs. Top priority should be given for developing this engineering characteristic. (See Figure 2.5)

Also, with the competitive benchmarking result, a clear idea is obtained on what product requirements will satisfy the customer. One can identify not only strengths and weaknesses, but also opportunities for breakthrough. Referring to the analysis of the ACB example, it is found that the main weaknesses are cost, not being able to move freely, and the frame being too

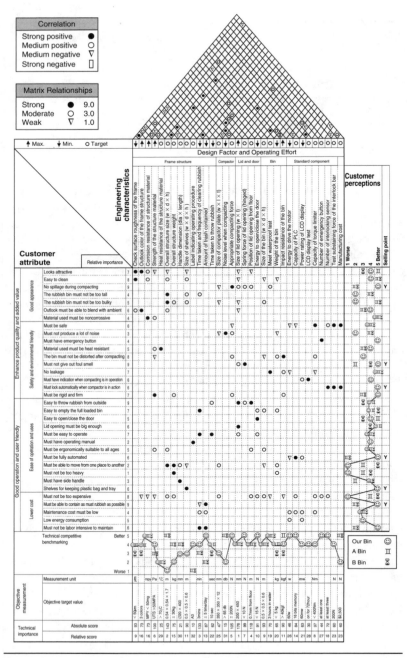

Figure 2.5   The completed HOQ (adapted from Sim, 2000).

heavy. If these could be improved upon, the competitiveness of the product would be enhanced.

The rest of this book will discuss and present some advanced issues and methods for the analysis of the HOQ. Note that not all will be needed all the time. On the other hand, it is important to be equipped with tools to handle unusual problems and issues. Quality function deployment can be much more useful than what has been traditionally described.

RECENT DEVELOPMENT OF THE QFD METHODOLOGY

Although QFD has been proposed and put in use for several decades, it is still in its developmental stage. Various research topics have been identified and studied with the aim of solving difficulties and problems, thereby leading to an improved methodology. A literature review reveals that among these topics, considerable attention has been given to the voice of the customer analysis, determination of the optimal technical targets, simplification and computerization of the QFD process, and the use of artificial intelligence (AI).

This section mainly gives an overview of the recently discussed issues and some research questions related to QFD analysis. No details will be given here although several advanced concepts and techniques are mentioned. Some specific techniques will be discussed in detail later in this book. Readers can also find many references here from which further details can be found.

Analysis of the Voice of the Customer

When adopting QFD, the activities and operations of a company are driven by the voice of the customer. The voice of the customer is considered the backbone and input to the whole QFD process. Analysis of the voice of the customer plays an important role at the front-end stage of QFD since it is very important to have accurate representations of customer desires. This topic has been researched with a focus on identifying and understanding the true voice of the customer.

In the domain of market research, numerous well-developed techniques are related to customers and their requirements to various extents. Thus, many techniques have been used in QFD to help collect the voice of the customer. They include surveys, focus groups, interviews, customer complaints, direct observations, panels, and so on. (Shillito, 1994; Cohen, 1995).

Griffin and Hauser (1993) provided a comprehensive discussion on the voice of the customer, focusing on its identification, structuring, and prioritization. Some of their major findings include:

1. One-on-one interviews may be more cost effective than focus groups.

2. Twenty to 30 interviews are necessary to get information on 90 percent or more of customer needs.

3. Multiple analysts (four to six) should analyze the transcripts.

4. The customer-sort hierarchies seem to group needs to reflect how customers use the product, while team-consensus charts group needs to reflect how the firm builds the product.

5. Survey measures of importance can predict how customers will react to product concepts although there is no single best measure.

The Analytic Hierarchy Priority (AHP) is a multicriteria decision-making technique particularly useful for evaluating complex multiattribute alternatives involving subjective and intangible criteria. It allows decision makers to measure data consistency and stability. Many techniques, such as the utility model and the score model, are available for prioritizing customer requirements. Instead of solely relying on subjective judgments, however, the AHP is recently studied in Doukas et al. (1995), Wang et al. (1998), Kwong and Bai (2002) among others. For a similar purpose, the conjoint analysis was proposed to find the quality attributes most valuable to customers (Gustafsson et al., 1999; Pullman et al., 2002).

The voices of the customers are different from each other not only in terms of context and priority, but also in nature. Some customer needs can clearly be "delighting quality," while others may only be able to ensure that customers will not be unsatisfied. The Kano model divides product or service features into three distinct categories, that is, attractive, one-dimensional, and must-be, each of which affects customers in a different way (Kano et al., 1984). This model was combined with QFD for understanding the nature of the voice of the customer and for successful product development projects (Matzler et al., 1996; Matzler and Hinterhuber, 1998; Tan et al., 1999). Based on the Kano model, some researchers have also suggested ways of adjusting priorities for customer needs (for example, see Robertshaw, 1995).

Determination of the Technical Priority and Target Values

One of the advantages of QFD is that it links customer requirements to engineering characteristics qualitatively and quantitatively. Traditionally, engineering characteristics can be prioritized according to their additive impact on customer requirements using a relationship matrix and adopting a particular scale, for example, 1-3-9 or 1-5-9. Given limited resources, the prioritization is essential in guiding QFD users to make tradeoffs in the selection of different engineering characteristics.

Although the standard approach is easy to use, there are several issues involved in this prioritization phase that make for difficult application of QFD. These include the relatively arbitrary setting of numerical scale, the conversion of ordinal to cardinal scale, and the underutilization of the roof matrix. In response, various approaches have been proposed from different perspectives. For example, by extending Lyman's (1990) deployment normalization, Wasserman (1993) proposed a prioritization method that takes the correlations among the engineering characteristics into account. He also suggested the use of the technical importance as a cost index in prioritizing the allocation of resources.

As another example, Franceschini and Rossetto (1995) used multiple criteria decision aid methods to rank the engineering characteristics. This was compared with the traditional approach, leading to the conclusion that the avoidance of the rigid procedure of turning relationships from an ordinal into a cardinal scale could be achieved. Chan and Wu (1998) proposed two new techniques for better prioritization of engineering characteristics. The HOQ can be considered as a typical multiple attribute decision-marking process. The prioritization can also be viewed as assessing the performance of engineering characteristics. Wang (1999) considered QFD as a multicriteria decision problem and developed a new fuzzy outranking approach that is able to handle the evaluation results with linguistic terms or to prioritize the engineering characteristics.

Prioritizing engineering characteristics is important in allocating resources and guiding downstream analysis; but it provides the information in a general, nonspecific form. It may be desirable to determine the specific value for each engineering characteristic. From a design process viewpoint, Belhe and Kusiak (1996) modeled the problem of determining optimal values of design process variables to maximize the combined quality index of the critical design process variables. Based on multiattribute utility theory, their HOQ was interpreted and formulated as a multiobjective optimization problem with constraints derived from the HOQ and physical laws (Thurston and Locascio, 1993; Locascio and Thurston, 1998).

Given the availability of the technical benchmarking information, Franceschini and Rossetto (1997) developed an algorithm for designing the product's technical quality profile. This was further modified by Franceschini and Zappulli (1998) and applied to a real case for an important automobile firm. Kim (1997) developed a prescriptive modeling approach to determining the target values of engineering characteristics, which would maximize the overall customer satisfaction under the system and budget constraints. Some other related references dealing with optimization issues related to QFD are Kim et al. (2000), Fung et al. (2002), and Karsak (2003).

Franceschini and Rossetto (1998) formulated and solved the set-covering problem by utilizing a heuristic algorithm. By taking the cost of each engineering characteristic into account, Park and Kim (1998) developed a mathematical programming-based approach to determining an optimal set of engineering characteristics. Its aim was to maximize the total absolute technical importance rating from selected engineering characteristics, which represents the magnitude of customer satisfaction.

Simplification and Computerization of QFD

The QFD method is a complex process. One of the difficulties involved in applying it is the large size of an HOQ and subsequent matrices. It is not easy and is time consuming to have to assess the relationships between each customer attribute and engineering characteristic, and the correlations among the various engineering characteristics. Research work has been carried out on the HOQ size reduction, simple generation of relationships and correlations, simplified QFD procedures, and computerization of the QFD process.

Because of the relatively large size of the HOQ, Hunter and Landingham (1994) revised the HOQ by deleting less-important customer attributes and engineering characteristics. Viewing the risk involved in this approach, Kim et al. (1997) presented a formal approach to reducing the size of an HOQ chart using the concept of design decomposition combined with multiattribute value theory. The HOQ chart was decomposed into smaller subproblems that can be solved efficiently and independently. Kihara et al. (1994) described a disciplined approach to using a type of Quantification Method in QFD, which is a modeling technique of clustering diverse requirements into logical categories. By adopting factor analysis, Shin and Kim (1997) proposed a restructuring approach to creating a new HOQ with a reduced number of engineering characteristics. Shin et al. (1998) further developed a complexity reduction approach using correspondence analysis. It decomposes an HOQ into several matrices that are smaller in size and, thus, makes it easier to perform QFD in practice.

Focusing on easy generation of the correlations among engineering characteristics rather than on the reduction of the HOQ size, Franceschini and Rossetto (1998) proposed a partially automatic tool to indirectly define correlations among engineering characteristics. However, the presence of an induced dependence of the requirements is a necessary, but not sufficient, condition to state that two engineering characteristics are correlated. QFD users will play a role in confirming their real existence and judging between positive and negative signs.

Some simpler versions of QFD were proposed for its easier and faster usage. For example, Blitz QFD, as a streamlined approach, was developed for QFD teams that have constraints on time, people, and money (ReVelle et al., 1997). It demonstrates the selection and deployment of only the top most important ranked customer needs. Seven steps are included when applying Blitz QFD, namely, gathering the voice of the customer, sorting the verbatims received from the customers, structuring the customer needs, analyzing the customer needs structure, prioritizing customer needs, deploying the prioritized customer needs, and analyzing only the important relationships in detail. In the case of another simplified version of QFD, McLaurin and Bell (1993) introduced and used a four-step model called customer requirements analysis and deployment, a structured method for discovering customers' requirements and getting customer feedback on company performance.

In addition to the standard commercial QFD software systems (see, for example, Moskowitz and Kim, 1997), other computerized QFD systems were developed to serve different purposes. For example, in order to gain well-organized information so that customer requirements are consistently met, Sriraman et al. (1990) suggested the use of object-oriented databases in QFD because they are able to store, organize, and manipulate both customer requirements and product information. Huang and Mak (2002) presented a study on the use of the World Wide Web to provide QFD services.

Due mainly to limitations when implementing QFD as a set of paper forms, Wolfe (1994) developed a hypertext-based group decision support system, which could provide support for strategic planning at the inception of each major system, and support for requirements management, coordination, and control throughout the development process. To implement QFD as a group productivity tool instead of an individual one, Balthazard and Gargeya (1995) proposed to develop an integrative technology that meshes QFD and group support system initiatives. Maier (1995) suggested the representation of an entire hierarchy of QFD matrices in a single rectangular grid, which allows full QFD analysis on standard computer spreadsheets instead of special-purpose packages.

Trappey et al. (1996) gave a formal QFD methodology for the retail industry and built a computerized retail QFD system. Moskowitz and Kim

(1997) developed an interactive, self-contained, and novice-friendly QFD decision support system prototype that allows one to build an HOQ, analyze system interrelationships, and obtain optimal target engineering characteristic values.

Use of Artificial Intelligence and Other Techniques

Another emerging trend in the development of the QFD methodology is the use of artificial intelligence (AI) and other related techniques. Reich (1996) discussed the AI-supported QFD and concentrated on the benefits that AI technology can offer to QFD in the processes of information acquisition, use, and communication, for example, natural language processing, grid-based knowledge acquisition tools, case-based reasoning, and IBIS-like information structure. In particular, an architecture of a computational QFD for embedding QFD tools and their AI supporting tools are presented.

Expert systems provide advantages of availability, consistency, and testability by capturing and manipulating the knowledge of human experts. The applicability of expert systems in quality management and QFD has been discussed (Crossfield and Dale, 1991; Bird, 1992). To avoid the need to input large amounts of data and the necessity of estimating values on a rather subjective basis in QFD, Zhang et al. (1996) suggested a machine learning approach in which a neural network automatically determines the data by learning from examples. Kim et al. (1998) proposed a knowledge-based approach for constructing, classifying, and managing HOQ charts. With a rule-type knowledge base, time and effort can be reduced by analyzing an HOQ chart base classified along similar cases. Karsak et al. (2003) presented a combined analytic network process and goal programming approach in the aid of decision making with QFD.

The use of fuzzy set theory (Zadeh, 1965) in QFD has received considerable attention recently. Masud and Dean (1993) reported an investigation of how QFD analyses can be performed when the input variables are treated as linguistic variables with values expressed as fuzzy numbers. Khoo and Ho (1996) developed an approach centered on the application of possibility theory and fuzzy arithmetic to address the ambiguity involved in various relationships. Fung et al. (1998) proposed a hybrid system that incorporates the principles of QFD, AHP, and fuzzy set theory to tackle the complex and often imprecise problem domain encountered in customer requirement management. Other related references can be found in Chan et al. (1999), Temponi et al. (1999), Kim et al. (2000), Sohn (2001), and Kwong and Bai (2002).

Chapter 3
Future Voice of the Customer

Despite numerous discussions on the voice of the customer (VOC) in the literature, the scope has often been limited to customers' current requirements. Under rapidly changing environments, customers change their opinions and thus have requirements that are more dynamic than static. Traditional QFD collects and utilizes customer requirements in the present tense, that is, only the current voice of the customer is designed into the final product. Due to the time lag from the collection of the customer requirements to the design and manufacturing of the products, then to the marketing of the final product, until the customers actually purchase and use the products, customers' preferences may have changed. There is, thus, a time dimension to be factored in when the voice of the customer is discussed.

The voice of the customer can be divided into two types based on the possibility of quantifying the attributes. That is, the voice of the customer can be *qualitative* VOC and *quantitative* VOC. The qualitative VOC defines primarily what customers want and need. The quantitative VOC basically represents how customers prioritize their wants and needs, that is, the importance of customer requirements. Both types of VOCs are mapped onto the voice of the engineer using the HOQ. QFD users can come up with a list of technical characteristics based on customers' various requirements. Relationship numerical values are used to map the quantitative information so that the relative contributions of technical characteristics to overall customer satisfaction can be calculated.

Focusing mainly on the quantitative aspect, this chapter extends the scope of the VOC into the future. In this chapter, the problem with the traditional voice of the customer is discussed and the concept of the future voice of the customer is proposed. Methods are developed to serve the purpose of predicting the future importance of customer requirements. Given sufficient historical data, a forward planning approach is proposed by using forecasting techniques. In particular, the exponential smoothing technique is suggested and discussed. This method is especially suitable when the data exhibit a trend that should be captured. For the case of no historical data, the fuzzy trend analysis method has been developed. Specifically, fuzzy set theory is used to quantify vague linguistic data gathered from preliminary surveys or discussions with customers. This is to quantify and incorporate the trend of importance into the calculation of the final importance in the form of a fuzzy trend.

VOC WITH A FUTURE DIMENSION

As pointed out, it takes time to complete the desired product after gathering the required VOC and after conducting the QFD analysis. However, in traditional QFD, we collect customers' voices and then ask them to rate the importance as it is today. It is, however, important to consider what will happen after a product is designed, manufactured, and shipped to customers. The importance of each customer requirement might be the same as before or it might have increased or decreased. Earlier customer needs may have disappeared, and new needs might have been added and may come into play at a later time.

Given a changing VOC, the final product may not deliver to the customers what they want and desire at the time of delivery. In other words, traditional QFD is driven by the *past* voice of the customer. However, since the final product may only meet customers' past requirements, and there may not be total customer satisfaction if their future requirements are not considered, one might go so far as to say that use of the traditional VOC in QFD could only satisfy customers' past needs. Hence, a company may not be able to keep pace with customers' needs without considering the time dimension.

In a bid to solve the above problem, a dynamic approach to QFD was developed by Adiano and Roth (1994) to translate customer wants and needs into relevant product and process parameters. Using feedback loops, the approach incorporates updated customer satisfaction data and dynamically links evolving requirements directly back into the manufacturing and value chain processes. This reactive approach may not work well in those industries where technology and customer requirements change rapidly. In addition, it is necessary to collect more data such that a relatively accurate conclusion can be drawn. Consequently, more surveys will be conducted if the survey is the way of collecting VOCs. It will require more time and effort for QFD users to complete the task of collecting a large amount of data.

From a new product development point of view, this problem can be partially solved by shortening product development cycle time (see for example, LaBahn et al., 1996). But this might not be enough to maintain competitiveness since the time lag is still there even though the cycle time may be reduced. In addition, reducing the product development cycle time may not be easily achieved. Hence, this type of solution while viable, may nevertheless not address the issue of future needs.

A more proactive approach to dealing with the changing VOC would be a time-based extension by listening to the future voice of the customer. Similar to the traditional VOC, there are two types of future VOCs. From a qualitative point of view, it includes new customer needs and requirements that may appear in the future. Quantitatively, the future VOC contains the new prioritization of customer requirements.

From a time-based perspective, it can be seen that the future VOC and the traditional VOC possess almost the same characteristics except for different time periods. A major difference between the future and current voices of the customer is that few customers know the future voice of the customer at present, while the current voice of the customer is already known clearly by most customers. That is, at present, most customers are not clear about the future voice of the customer and even do not realize it, but most customers will come to know it in the future.

Shillito (1994) remarked that little attention has been paid to the time dimension of the VOC, especially for very novel products or in rapidly changing industries, for example, the information technology (IT) industry. To remain competitive, it is necessary to listen to the voice of the customer in the future, so that it will allow us to look at what future product/process/systems designs will be considered to be competitive. Hence, there is a strong need to study and develop procedures that can be used in extending the VOCs into the future. Moreover, two situations should be taken into consideration, that is, with and without sufficient historical data.

USE OF THE FUTURE VOC

After projecting and identifying the future voice of the customer, either through a survey or another method discussed earlier, QFD practitioners can use the future-oriented information in the QFD process. In this section, several operational and implementation issues with respect to the use of the future VOC in QFD are discussed.

Validating the Future VOC

When using the future VOC in QFD, one is often interested in estimating the acceptability of a future product. If the future VOC is successfully identified, the future product will meet customers' requirements and they will accept it. However, if the incorrect future VOC is identified and incorporated into the QFD process, customers may not accept the future product because it does not meet their requirements. Thus, correct identification of the future VOC is a prerequisite to the successful implementation of this methodology. It is clear that techniques should be developed to protect a company from incorrect or inaccurate future VOCs.

One simple approach to validating the future VOC is to test whether it is really what ordinary customers need and want, as von Hippel (1986) suggested for the use of lead user analysis. Lead users are existing or potential customers who are better able to identify future opportunities for emerging concepts or new products. In this case, after capturing the future VOC from lead users, some ordinary customers are randomly chosen and they are asked to further express their opinions on the possibility of these particular voices. Ordinary customers may or may not take lead users' needs as their future requirements. By seeking approval from ordinary customers, QFD practitioners will have more confidence in the use of the future VOC for future product development.

Note that conclusions made by this method should be carefully interpreted. For instance, when the future VOC identified by lead users is too novel from ordinary customers' point of view, they are relatively more likely to make a wrong judgment and to oppose these voices, even though in fact they will eventually accept them. Hence, QFD teams should carefully analyze the responses from the ordinary customers, and if necessary, more in-depth interviews with them should be conducted.

Incorporating the Future VOC

Two possible formats may be adopted in QFD analysis to incorporate the future VOC. The first one is to use two separate HOQs with the current and the future VOC respectively. The other format is to use a single HOQ with the integrated VOC obtained by combining the current and future VOCs.

The use of two separate HOQs is first presented. The current VOC is considered as the input to the first HOQ, which is very similar to the traditional HOQ except that QFD practitioners understand that only the present VOCs are included. Figure 3.1 shows part of an HOQ based on the current VOC for a Web page design. For simplicity and easy illustration, only two

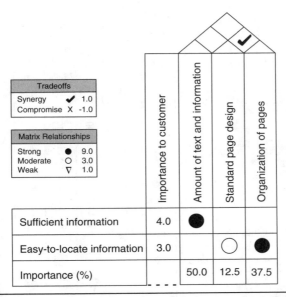

Figure 3.1 Some elements in HOQ with the current VOC for a Web page design study.

customer requirements are included here, namely, "sufficient information" and "easy-to-locate information."

The second HOQ is based on the future VOCs that have been identified by lead users. Figure 3.2 shows part of an HOQ with the future VOC for a Web page design. For example, another customer need—"interesting Web page"—may be identified by lead users, and its importance is identified as a "4" using a 1–5 point scale. Based on this information, the QFD team then develops the corresponding technical characteristics, and their relationships with future customer attributes, correlations, and technical importance. It should be noted that sometimes it is better for lead users to get involved with the product development team because they may be able to come up with good ideas, especially on technical characteristics. The information provided in Figure 3.2 that is driven by the future VOC would be different from those in the first HOQ. The team then makes decisions on what kinds of information would be included and further employed in downstream QFD processes.

Another way to incorporate the future VOC into the QFD process is to use a single HOQ. In this method, the current and future VOCs are first combined into the so-called integrated VOC, which includes both the qualitative and quantitative VOC after the QFD team has made compromises

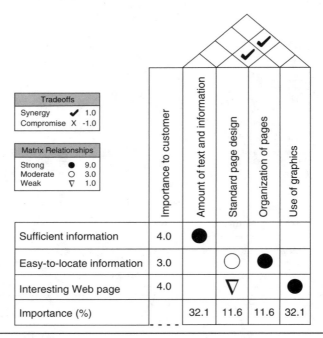

Figure 3.2 Incorporating new elements of HOQ with the future VOC for a Web page design study. Note that an item is added compared with Figure 3.1.

and trade-offs between the current and future VOCs. For example, the QFD team may believe that the new customer need of "interesting Web page" will be required by the general market in the future, but its corresponding importance value may be "3" instead of "4". Following the traditional HOQ construction procedures, other submatrices are completed based on the integrated VOC, and they are used in subsequent QFD activities.

The difference between Figure 3.2 and Figure 3.3 is that the former HOQ is purely based on the future VOC, while the latter is based on the combined information from both the current and future VOCs. Note that the weights are changed and hence the decision made based on different HOQs could be different.

The first method, that is, two HOQs with the current and future VOC, requires more time and effort to develop. The QFD team has to complete the construction of two HOQs based on the current and future VOCs respectively. In the second method, one HOQ with integrated VOC is used and less time and effort would be needed for the construction of the HOQ.

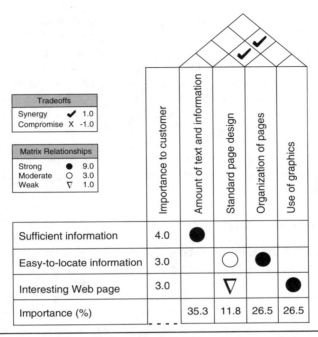

Figure 3.3　One HOQ with integrated VOC for a Web page design study. Note that the weights are changed compared with Figure 3.2.

Specifically, after combining the current and future VOC into the integrated VOC, QFD team members can proceed to construct the HOQ in the usual way. Therefore, in the case where there is a high requirement on the product development cycle time, the second method is preferred and only one HOQ needs to be constructed based on the integrated VOC.

Using two HOQs based on the current and future VOC separately, however, allows us to really look at what the future could be and how to meet these future needs. By constructing an HOQ solely driven by the future VOC, we can understand what customers want and need in the near future from a leading-edge position. It can also provide us with specific solutions to meet these requirements from a technical point of view. If one HOQ is used, there is a chance that we will lose some valuable information for possible technical breakthroughs or the emergence of innovative product features.

As far as the responsibility of team members is concerned, the marketing people and engineers may participate in incorporating the future VOC to varying degrees. When using one HOQ with an integrated VOC, the marketing people may play a more important role than the engineers can. They will take more responsibility for combining both the current and future VOCs into the integrated VOC before the construction of the HOQ, since they are closer to customers and more familiar with their needs.

On the other hand, engineers may take a leading position in the construction of two HOQs. They should come up with technical characteristics for the current VOC. More critically, they need to also find out technical characteristics for the future VOC, some of which may not be technically available. They have to spend more time and effort to discuss, test, and eventually figure them out. Thus, the two-HOQs method is more applicable to situations where a company has considerable strength in its technical capabilities.

Combination Strategies

As discussed, ordinary customers provide QFD practitioners with their voices in the present tense, while lead users offer possibilities of predicting ordinary customers' future requirements. The QFD team should utilize both information sources. One way is to combine them into an integrated VOC (Figure 3.4). Three typical strategies are discussed below.

1. *Ordinary customer-based strategy.* In this scenario, the integrated VOC is mostly composed of the current VOC, and little future VOC is adopted. It is basically current VOC oriented and the main activity executors are ordinary customers. Some of the main activities may include removing some of the future VOC that are considered not to be true for ordinary customers, deleting some of the current VOC that will not appear after considering lead users' suggestions, and reprioritizing integrated customer requirements. It should be noted that it is necessary for QFD facilitators to make their own decision when there exist significant differences among the opinions of ordinary customers.

2. *Lead user-based strategy.* This scenario represents a different situation from the ordinary customer-based strategy. Under this scenario, most of the integrated VOC is transformed from the future VOC, with little adoption of the current VOC. The main activity executors are lead users, who are in charge of removing some of the current VOC that will not appear in the future, and reprioritizing the integrated customer requirements after considering ordinary customers' voices. When using this future VOC–driven strategy, it is necessary to test the integrated VOC to seek ordinary customers' approval on the new product concept for protection from incorrect future VOCs.

3. *QFD facilitator-based strategy.* This combination strategy aims at a compromise of the above polar situations. The main activity executors are QFD facilitators. Both the current and future VOCs are considered by the

QFD facilitators and each of them is partly adopted and combined into the integrated VOC. The activities involved in this method are mainly removing some of the future VOC that will not be accepted by ordinary customers, deleting some of the current VOC that will not appear in the future, combining the future and current VOCs into the integrated VOC, and reprioritizing the integrated requirements.

Some Implementation Issues

It is often desirable to decide whether and when to be future oriented, and to what degree. That is, the product development team wants to know how much attention should be paid to listening to the future VOC and how much to the current VOC. The issue of the future VOC versus the present VOC is one of risk versus benefit. The future is uncertain where nobody knows exactly what will happen. However, if a company can undertake the risk or manage to avoid or reduce it, and also adopt a systematic way of understanding future needs, it would have a higher possibility of receiving tremendous benefit.

The three combination strategies discussed above represent three different attitudes toward the issue of risk versus benefit. Moreover, different methods should be applied to different situations where applicable and suitable. Thus, an optimal balance between the future and the present is always desirable. It is a critical decision between the future versus present orientations since there are no clear-cut measures, criteria, or benchmarks to act as indicators (Samli, 1996).

Nonetheless, there are two guidelines for determining the optimal balance point between the future and current VOCs:

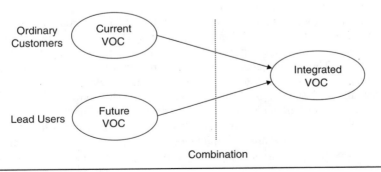

Combination

Figure 3.4   Combining the current and future VOCs.

- First, a company should focus more on the future VOC when it finds itself in the following circumstances: highly competitive, no-innovation-no-survival, can undertake risk, and/or where the speed to market is critical.

- Second, the current VOC should play a more important role under the following circumstances: the company cannot undertake risk (once wrong, no survival), the competitiveness and requirement on speed to market are not very high, and/or innovative products are needed but not essential.

Based on the use of the future voice of the customer in QFD, the following implications can be obtained from a managerial perspective. First, customers play an important role in a successful business. They can provide more information than a company expects. Taking a customer-driven approach, a company should capture and understand what customers want and desire. Only after knowing these can a company take appropriate actions and provide suitable products/services to meet and even exceed customers' expectations. Marketing research helps obtain the voice of the customer, and QFD is a useful tool in that it utilizes this information further by linking marketing and other functions, for example, engineering and manufacturing. Among them, the marketing function has a leadership role in administering the QFD process (O'Neal and LaFief, 1992).

As discussed earlier, the voice of the customer is sophisticated and has a time dimension. Thus, the second implication is that listening to the current voice of the customer is important, but it would be better to take a more proactive approach to project and capture future customer requirements and embed them into the future products and services, especially in rapidly changing industries. Such an approach can enable a company to develop and launch new products or new versions of existing products, even though they may not be as yet widely acceptable. By doing so, the company might have a higher possibility of marketing the right products or services to the right customers at the right time.

In addition, deciding whether the input of QFD is current or future oriented is a strategic decision, and this is always critical. It is management who should undertake this responsibility and try to make an appropriate selection. Thus, management support is important for listening to the future voice of the customer. Internal factors and external circumstances must be carefully assessed and evaluated before choosing the optimal balance point between the current and future voices of the customer. These organizational and environmental factors that management should consider when making decisions include, but are not limited to, technology capability, competitiveness, time to market, risk undertaking capability, and product marketability.

USE OF FORECASTING METHODS

In the previous section we discussed the approach of directly obtaining the future needs and the methods of combining the needs. In many practical situations, the future needs are very uncertain. The customers may not have the information about the technological changes that could occur. On the other hand, things are predictable with additional information. One example is the CPU speed and hard disk size. When designing a product, it is possible to forecast the trend and hence the future needs of the customers.

Forecasting Requirement Importance

Forecasting techniques for technical decisions have been in use for several decades. Forecasting is very important in many fields, such as business, industry, government, and education. Prediction of future events must be incorporated into the decision-making process as many people have concluded. For example, by making good forecasts, a company can have a better understanding of the likely growth of markets in the context of the expected economic environment, and can monitor its potential for achieving greater customer satisfaction.

A wide variety of forecasting methods are available. They range from the most basic methods, such as the use of the most recent observation as a forecast, to highly complex approaches, such as simultaneous systems. Three categories of forecasting methods are usually identified, that is, judgmental, quantitative, and technological. Among them, quantitative methods have received the widest coverage.

In QFD analysis, the importance of the VOC usually follows trends. For example, some important items may not be that important when they are already satisfied, while other items gain in importance. Here, double exponential smoothing, which is one of the most widely used and useful forecasting techniques in time-series modeling, is used to predict the importance of the VOC in QFD. Note that the single exponential smoothing is known to lag behind the trend, and hence double exponential is used.

The Double Exponential Smoothing Technique

The double exponential smoothing technique can be used for forecasting time series data that has a linear trend. The relatively straightforward Brown's method is discussed here (Hanke and Reitsch, 1998), although other methods are equally applicable.

Suppose the importance of the ith customer requirement given by the customer in the tth period is x_{it}, then, the forecast of the ith customer voice p periods ahead in the future, $\hat{x}_{i(t+p)}$ is given by

$$\hat{x}_{i(t+p)} = a_{it} + b_{it}\, p \qquad (3.1)$$

where a_{it} is the difference between the exponential smoothed values

$$a_{it} = A_{it} - A'_{it} \qquad (3.2)$$

and b_{it} is a slope measurement that can change over the series

$$b_{it} = \frac{\alpha}{1-\alpha}\left(A_{it} - A'_{it}\right) \qquad (3.3)$$

and
$$A_{it} = \alpha x_{it} + (1-\alpha)\, A_{i(t-1)} \qquad (3.4)$$

is the exponential smoothed value of x_{it} at time t and

$$A'_{it} = \alpha A_{it} + (1-\alpha)\, A'_{i(t-1)} \qquad (3.5)$$

is the double exponential smoothed value of x_{it} at time t.

Following the above method, the importance of every VOC in Period $t+1$ can be obtained. By using forecasts as the importance of the customer's voice in Period $t+1$, the approximate analysis of the future VOC can be achieved. Based on the forecasts on importance, the corresponding HOQ can be built, which helps QFD users make subsequent decisions; such as resource allocation and part deployment.

If QFD users follow the standard method for calculating the importance of the technical responses, the forecast weight of the jth technical response in p periods ahead is then given by:

$$\hat{a}_{j(t+p)} = \sum_{i=1}^{n} R_{ij}\,\hat{x}_{i(t+p)} \qquad (3.6)$$

where

$\hat{a}_{j(t+p)}$ = the weight for the jth technical response in p periods ahead

R_{ij} = the weight assigned to relationships in the relationship matrix.

Implementation

One assumption of the above method is that it requires the company to have *sufficient historical data* so that the forecasting can be effective. This actually requires a company to keep track of the historical data and information, which is important in quality analysis in general. In the case that sufficient historical data is not available, a rough analysis based on some previous data, might be obtained to help make a preliminary decision.

The value assigned to α is one of the keys to accurate forecasting analysis. If it is desired that the prediction be stable, a small value of α is required. If a rapid response to the change in the pattern of observations is desired, a larger value of α is appropriate. One general method of estimating α is an iterative procedure that minimizes the mean square error (MSE) calculated by

$$MSE = \frac{\sum_{t=1}^{n}\left(x_{it} - \hat{x}_{it}\right)^2}{n} \tag{3.7}$$

In the above forecasting process, only the analysis of historical data is used to generate the final forecast; the judgment or opinion of the analyst is not utilized in the process. In fact, the use of good judgment is an essential component of all good forecasting techniques. Good judgment is required to decide on the pattern of data and to interpret the results of the data analyzed. It sometimes makes up a major portion of the analysis (Hanke and Reitsch, 1998).

Nowadays, because of the rapidly changing technology, an estimated 25 percent of existing technology is replaced every year. Obviously, even a very sophisticated forecast based on historical data might miss the wide margin under these circumstances. Innovation and R&D will change the external conditions of a company, and these will lead to changing customer needs. Special attention, therefore, should be put to identifying changing external conditions and new customer needs. If new VOCs are identified to be important, it should be incorporated into the QFD analysis. This constitutes an important part in the overall forecasting process.

Technological developments increase the need for companies to be much more alert to changes in customer requirements and expectations. Still, historical patterns can provide at least some clues about the future in many businesses. Forecasting studies involving the combination of these two should be applied in QFD analysis in order to yield more accurate and cost-effective forecasts.

For ease of implementation, the use of the above forecasting methods in QFD analysis can be summarized by the following procedures:

1. Analyze the data of the importance of customer requirements from several periods in order to identify a pattern that can be used to describe it.

2. The pattern is extrapolated, or extended, into the future in order to prepare a forecast of the importance of customer requirements resting on the assumption that the pattern that has been identified will continue in the future.

3. Based on the historical data, match the appropriate forecasting model to the pattern of the available time series data.

4. Estimate the time series components, and use the estimates to compute a forecast of the importance of customer requirements.

5. Use other judgmental forecasting techniques or technical forecasting to identify other factors, such as new customer requirements due to the change of external conditions.

6. Use the forecast of the importance of the customer requirements in the HOQ and calculate the prioritization of the technical responses.

7. Check the results and revise any part of the HOQ if needed.

An Illustrative Example

In order to illustrate the forecasting-based planning approach, an example is presented in this section. The data used for the construction of the HOQ is adapted from Islam and Liu (1995) in designing a tourist camp stove.

Suppose the company has already done the product design and quality analysis using QFD for five periods and has obtained a different importance of each customer need in each period separately. The VOC and its relative importance in each period are shown in Table 3.1.

Based on the historical data of the past five periods, the general trends of the importance of different VOCs can be easily identified. There are obvious upper trends in the three customer requirements of "lightweight," "heats quickly," and "refillable." On the other hand, downward trends were reflected in "very compact" and "gas-ready available." Whereas, "operates quietly," "no repairs needed," and "can simmer" exhibit neither an increase nor a decrease in their importance.

Since the company has been using QFD for many periods, based on the trend pattern of historical data, management decided to use the double

Table 3.1 Historical importance data of customer requirements.

VOCs	Period 1	Period 2	Period 3	Period 4	Period 5
Very compact	0.26	0.21	0.19	0.15	0.14
Lightweight	0.05	0.06	0.07	0.08	0.09
Lights easily	0.03	0.05	0.05	0.04	0.04
Very stable	0.40	0.30	0.32	0.20	0.30
Operates quietly	0.02	0.05	0.05	0.05	0.05
Heats quickly	0.06	0.10	0.12	0.15	0.16
No repairs needed	0.01	0.01	0.01	0.02	0.02
Can simmer	0.02	0.01	0.01	0.01	0.01
Burns long with least weight	0.02	0.03	0.01	0.10	0.02
Refillable	0.02	0.06	0.07	0.11	0.12
Gas-ready available	0.12	0.12	0.08	0.05	0.03

exponential smoothing method to analyze and project the importance of the VOC in Period 6. Using the equations in the previous section and after some standard calculations, the importance of the VOC in Period 5 and the forecasts of the VOC in Period 6 are presented in Table 3.2. The second column contains the importance of the VOC in Period 5, which was also shown in Table 3.1. Different smoothing constants are used and they are given in the third column.

By comparing the forecast importance with that of the previous period, the trend of any possible changes can be easily identified. For example, during the past five periods, customers considered that the requirement "very compact" is becoming less important. Following the same trend, the forecast of this customer need was 0.1, which is smaller compared with 0.14 for Period 5.

Suppose that judgmental forecasting did not reveal any major change in the external conditions and no new VOCs were identified to add because of little technological innovation in the current period. An HOQ based on the forecasting results for Period 6 can then be built. The complete HOQ is shown in Figure 3.5. To investigate the difference between technical priority based on current data in Period 5 and the one with forecasts in Period 6, the HOQ is built in such a way that it contains data from both periods. The technical importance values shown in Figure 3.5 were calculated based on Equation (3.6).

From Figure 3.5, the difference between the ranking of technical responses with input data from Period 5 and that driven by the forecasts for Period 6 can be easily observed. It can be seen that not only the absolute importance of the technical responses changed in Period 6, but the technical

Table 3.2   The forecasts of importance value for Period 6.

VOCs	Period 5	α	Period 6
Very compact	0.14	0.1	0.100
Lightweight	0.09	0.2	0.100
Lights easily	0.04	0.1	0.045
Very stable	0.30	0.1	0.214
Operates quietly	0.05	0.1	0.062
Heats quickly	0.16	0.1	0.193
No repairs needed	0.02	0.1	0.023
Can simmer	0.01	0.1	0.006
Burns long with least weight	0.02	0.1	0.057
Refillable	0.12	0.1	0.151
Gas-ready available	0.03	0.1	0.005

ranking did as well. For instance, the technical response "volume" became less important when QFD users adopted the forecasting approach. Specifically, it ranked second with importance data in Period 5; it ranked fourth when using forecast data. Taking technical response "average boiling time" as another example, its ranking order changed from third to second. The increase of ranking order suggests that "average boiling time" became more important. It leads to the conclusion that QFD users should pay more attention to this technical response when adopting the proposed proactive approach. Similar analysis can be performed on other technical responses.

USE OF FUZZY TREND ANALYSIS

The forecasting-based method presented in the previous section was developed in the case that sufficient historical data are available. However, in practice this assumption may be invalid. Let us take a look at Table 3.1. In this table, it is assumed that historical data of each customer importance are available. Nevertheless, it is possible that new customer needs were identified and added during these periods. Subsequently, the historical importance data become insufficient, which will result in incorrect forecasts. Another extreme case is where there is no historical importance data for each need. This is a common situation where companies just start to use QFD or apply it to a new product design.

In traditional QFD, the planning matrix is used in the HOQ to adjust customers' raw priority for each customer need. The planning matrix is one

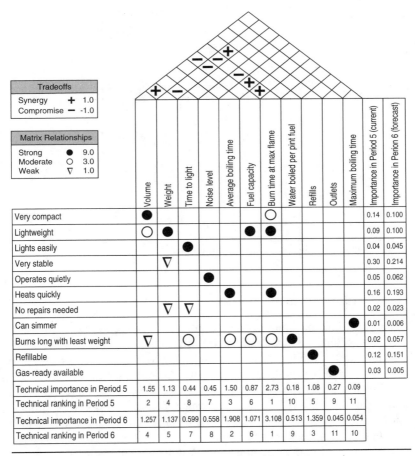

Figure 3.5   The HOQ with current and predicted importance values.

part of the HOQ that contains strategic marketing information and planning decisions. Several adjustment factors are used in the traditional planning matrix. Two typical ones are customer satisfaction benchmarking (competitive analysis) and sales point (see Figure 3.6). For more information about competitive analysis and sales point in the planning matrix, see Cohen (1995) and Mizuno and Akao (1994). For other adjustment factors and criteria in the planning matrix, see, for example, Shillito (1994).

Customer attributes	Importance	Our current product	Competitor 1	Competitor 2	Our future product	Improvement ratio	Sales point	Final importance
		Competitive analysis						
Customer attributes	...	...	...	...	...	...	...	...

Figure 3.6 Planning matrix in traditional QFD.

Trend of Importance

In the traditional planning matrix, all information such as raw importance, competitive analysis, and sales point are gathered in the present tense. Listening to the future voice of the customer will enable organizations to remain competitive and truly capture what the customer needs.

Trend analysis can help QFD users extend the quantitative VOC into the future. Specifically, one new adjustment factor, named trend of importance, can be incorporated into the traditional planning matrix. It helps the quantitative VOC contain the information with a future dimension. The use of trend analysis in the planning matrix can be seen in Figure 3.7.

Trend analysis for the importance of each customer requirement can be conducted through a customer survey. In traditional QFD, customers can be asked to provide what they want and desire. They are then asked to prioritize their needs and to rate the satisfaction level for each customer need. They can furthermore be asked to express their opinions on the trend of importance. For example, one typical question for trend analysis may be "Based on your knowledge and according to your estimation, do you think this customer need (for example, 'easy to get the information I need') will become more important or less important, and to what degree?"

Obviously customers may not be able to estimate what the future importance could be in a numerical sense. Usually what they do is extend the present importance into the future by using language, such as "more

	Importance	*Trend of importance*	Competitive analysis			Our future product	Improvement ratio	Sales point	Final importance
			Our current product	Competitor 1	Competitor 2				
Customer attribute	...	...	...	...	...	...	...	...	...

Figure 3.7   Planning matrix with trend of importance.

important," "much more important," and so on. A rating scale for the trend of importance can be used for the trend analysis. See Table 3.3.

In this simplified rating scale, only five symbols are chosen to represent the trend of importance: ↑↑, ↑, ↓↓, ↓, and →. We have adopted this because it is easy to use and has been described in Shillito (1994).

The trend of importance for each customer requirement can be collected through customer surveys. Shillito (1994) argued that one useful method for collecting VOC information about the future is the Delphi method using a Delphi questionnaire. Ideally, with the help of marketing people, QFD users can gather the trend of importance through a survey or a questionnaire. Note that before a survey is conducted, respondents must be provided with enough background knowledge on the particular trend analysis. For example, the rating scale and related information must be clearly stated.

Armed with the trend of importance, QFD users can easily extend the quantitative VOC into the future and therefore acquire the desired and necessary information. Based on the trend analysis, they can detect which customer need importance value will increase or decrease in the future, and they can have an idea of how significantly the future importance will increase or decrease. Consequently, QFD users can adjust the importance according to the trend analysis. For example, on the basis of the trend analysis, if customers estimate that the importance value of a certain customer need will

Table 3.3   The rating scale for trend of importance.

Symbol	Descriptor
↑↑	Significant increase of importance
↑	Moderate increase of importance
↓↓	Significant decrease of importance
↓	Moderate decrease of importance
→	Status quo; small increase or decrease of importance

increase in the future, QFD users may increase the final importance so that the future information can be incorporated into QFD data.

Although the trend of importance is useful for decision making in meeting the future needs of customers, it is also clear that this newly proposed adjustment method is quite subjective; that is, it is not easy for QFD users to decide how much they should increase or decrease accordingly (Shen et al., 2001). In the next section, a method using fuzzy numbers is proposed to quantify the information acquired from the trend analysis.

The Use of Fuzzy Set Theory

In the previous section, the trend importance is proposed to listen to the future voice of the customer. In practice, it is difficult to make full use of information about the trend because usually they are linguistic variables that cannot be easily quantified and then incorporated into QFD via the planning matrix. In this section, fuzzy numbers are proposed to quantify the vague data on the future from the trend analysis. More specifically, the linguistic trend of importance (refer to Table 3.3) can be quantified through the use of fuzzy trend of importance rather than a crisp number.

1. *Basic fuzzy set theory.* Developed by Zadeh (1965), the fuzzy set theory is primarily concerned with quantifying vagueness in human thought and perception. Applying fuzzy set theory, the transition from vagueness to quantification can be performed as shown in Figure 3.8.

Figure 3.8   Transition from vagueness to quantification using fuzzy set theory.

To deal with the description about vagueness of an object, Zadeh (1965) proposed the membership function that associates with each object a grade of membership belonging to the interval [0, 1]. A fuzzy set is designated as:

$$\forall x \in X, \mu_A(x) \in [0,1]$$

where
$$\mu_A(x)$$

is the degree of membership, ranging from 0 to 1, of a vague predicate, A, over the universe of objects, X. Here X is a space set which can be real numbers, natural numbers, or integers.

A fuzzy number is a normal and convex fuzzy set with membership function $\mu(x)$ which both satisfies

$$\text{normality: } \mu_A(x) = 1 \text{, for at least one } x \in R$$

and

$$\text{convexity: } \mu_A(x^*) \geq \mu_A(x_1) \wedge \mu_A(x_2)$$

where
$$\mu_A(x) \in [0,1]$$

and
$$\forall x^* \in [x_1, x_2]$$

As a special type of fuzzy number, a triangular fuzzy number (TFN) can be defined as $P = (a,b,c)$. The parameters a, b, and c respectively represent the smallest possible value, the most promising value, and the largest possible value that can describe a fuzzy event. For the sake of simplicity, the symmetrical triangular fuzzy number is used to quantify the linguistic trend of importance. A symmetrical TFN P can be represented by the interval $[\alpha_1, \alpha_2]$, that is, $P = [\alpha_1, \alpha_2]$; see Figure 3.9.

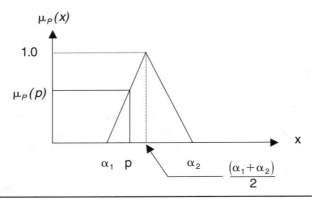

Figure 3.9   A symmetrical triangular fuzzy number *P*.

A typical membership function for a symmetrical TFN *P* can be expressed by:

$$\mu_P(p) = 1 - \frac{\left| p - \dfrac{\alpha_2 + \alpha_1}{2} \right|}{\dfrac{(\alpha_2 - \alpha_1)}{2}} \quad , \quad p \in P \tag{3.8}$$

2. *Using fuzzy set theory for the trend of importance.* Fuzzy set theory has been applied in QFD to describe the raw importance for each customer need, as well as the relationships between customer needs and technical characteristics (see, for example, Khoo and Ho, 1996). With the knowledge of fuzzy set theory, it is easy to quantify the linguistic variables about trend of importance into fuzzy numbers. To better understand the trend mechanism, fuzzy numbers P_i are used to represent the percentage change of importance.

The equations for calculating the final importance are expressed as follows:

$$P_f = P_0 + p \circ P_i \quad \text{for i} = 1,2,5$$

$$P_f = P_0 - p \circ P_i \quad \text{for i} = 3,4$$

where P_f is the final fuzzy importance; P_0 is the fuzzy importance derived from traditional methods; p is the crisp number for the importance derived from traditional methods; P_i is the ith fuzzy number for the percentage change in the trend analysis, and its definition is shown in Table 3.4. For more information about the arithmetic of fuzzy numbers, see, for example, Kaufmann and Gupta (1985).

3. *Some issues related to the use of fuzzy trend analysis.* Several issues related to the use of fuzzy trend analysis need to be discussed. First, note that the selection of fuzzy numbers depends on different QFD users and applications. That is to say, different QFD users may choose different fuzzy numbers (the value of percentage change); the same QFD users may also choose different fuzzy numbers for different QFD applications. The purpose here is to describe how fuzzy numbers can be used to quantify linguistic variables and be integrated into the QFD analysis for better decision making in product design and development.

The second issue is with regard to the levels of trend analysis. Use of the notations here is from Shillito (1994). As mentioned earlier, it is better to use more levels to conduct the trend analysis. From this definition, it can be easily seen that more levels are better since QFD users will have more choices to set the fuzzy numbers. If there are more choices to define the trend analysis, obviously the interval for each fuzzy number will be smaller. Therefore, more precise information can be interpreted from the fuzzy trend of importance.

Third, it should be stated that the range of fuzzy numbers for the change of increase and decrease are different. When the importance for a certain customer need is a decreasing value, the upper limit of the fuzzy number is 100 percent, that is, the needs of customers will not appear any more at that time. However, when the importance is an increasing value, the limit could be much larger; that is, its future value could be double, triple,

Table 3.4 Definition of fuzzy numbers for the corresponding linguistic variables.

	Linguistic variable	Fuzzy number P_i (percentage change)
1	Significant increase of importance	[40%, 60%]
2	Moderate increase of importance	[20%, 40%]
3	Significant decrease of importance	[40%, 60%]
4	Moderate decrease of importance	[20%, 40%]
5	Status quo; small change	[−5%, 5%]

or even several times larger than the present value. Therefore, theoretically there is no upper limit for the fuzzy number where the importance value of a certain customer need is increasing.

An Illustrative Example

As an illustration of the mechanics of the above approach, let us consider the following example (see Table 3.5) adapted from Cohen (1995, p. 120). In this example, the QFD method is used in the software development process. It must be noted that the above customer needs belong to only one category of all the customer requirements, that is, "The program is a pleasure to use" as shown in Cohen (1995).

In Table 3.5, the trend of importance for each customer need is identified. For example, customers may argue that the importance for the customer need "Easy to get the information I need" will increase significantly in the future. Therefore, a two up-arrow symbol is drawn to show this future trend. For the customer need "Can adjust the cursor to move as quickly as I'd like," customers may suggest that its corresponding importance will decrease moderately in the future. Consequently, one down-arrow is used to indicate this future trend. As for the other customer needs, their importance trends are clearly shown in Table 3.5 using the arrow symbols defined in Table 3.3.

Table 3.5   Trend analysis: customer needs for software development.

Customer needs	Importance	Trend
Can customize to suit my working style	81	↑
Easy to get the information I need	80	↑↑
Controls under my fingertips	83	↓
Intuitive controls	84	→
Enables me to find things in the document quickly	48	↑
Offers lots of sizes, fonts, and design options	45	→
Able to see what the fonts look like as I'm choosing them	42	→
Can adjust the cursor to move as quickly as I like	49	↓

After conducting the trend analysis and identifying the trend of importance in the future, the equations for calculating the final importance are used. The decision and analyses should then be based on the importance for each VOC as they provide a better prediction of the future voice of the customer.

As discussed earlier, the fuzzy numbers could be different in various cases. In this illustrative example, the fuzzy numbers defined in Table 3.4 are used to implement the calculation. The results are shown in Figure 3.6.

In Figure 3.10, two new columns were added compared with the traditional planning matrix, namely, "Trend of importance" and "Final importance" (fuzzy numbers). Comparing column "Adjusted Importance" (without future information) with column "Final Importance" (with future information), it can be easily seen that there are differences between these two columns.

Take the two customer needs "Intuitive controls" and "Enables me to find things in the document quickly" as examples. After the traditional QFD analysis, the former need ranks higher than the latter need (14 vs. 11). However, from the trend analysis it is found that the latter need will become more important in the future although the increase is not very significant, while the former need's importance still remains the same. Using the fuzzy numbers suggested in Table 3.4, the final importance of each customer need is calculated as a fuzzy number, and from the final importance, we may conclude that the latter need will be prioritized higher than the former need in the future, [13.3, 15.4] vs. [13.3, 14.7].

DISCUSSION

This chapter examined the time dimension of the voice of the customer and concluded that it is dynamic in nature. *Merely listening to the current voice of the customer is not enough.* For QFD users, what decision makers should know is the so-called "future voice of the customer." By listening to the future voice of customer and taking a proactive approach, companies will be able to remain competitive in a rapidly changing marketplace.

To meet the challenge due to the changing voice of the customer, two approaches were developed in this chapter by focusing on quantitative approaches. One is based on statistical forecasting of customer trend, and a second on using fuzzy trend analysis.

For a company with several years' experience using QFD, forecasting techniques can be used to help the decision makers to analyze the trend of VOC, and thereby get a further and rapid look at the market for future products. The double exponential smoothing forecasting technique is used to project the future importance of VOCs when the historical data pattern possesses

	Importance	Trend of importance	Our current product	Competitor	Our future product	Improvement ratio	Sales point	Adjusted importance (%)	Final importance (fuzzy numbers)
Can customize to suit my working style	81	↑	4.6	3.8	4.6	1.00	1.5	19	[22.8, 26.6]
Easy to get the information I need	81	↑↑	4.7	4.6	4.7	1.00	1.2	16	[22.4, 25.6]
Controls under my fingertips	83	↓	3.1	4.4	4.4	1.42	1.2	15	[9, 12]
Intuitive controls	84	→	2.9	2.8	3.3	1.14	1.5	14	[13.3, 14.7]
Enables me to find things in the document quickly	48	↑	3.1	4.4	4.5	1.45	1.5	11	[13.3, 15.4]
Offers lots of size, font, and design options	45	→	4.6	3.8	4.6	1.00	1.5	11	[10.5, 11.6]
Able to see what the fonts look like as I'm choosing them	42	→	4.7	4.6	4.7	1.00	1.2	8	[7.6, 8.4]
Can adjust the cursor to move as quickly as I'd like	49	↓	2.9	2.8	2.9	1.00	1.0	5	[3, 4]

Figure 3.10 The planning matrix for software development with fuzzy trend.

a linear trend and irregular fluctuations. Although it requires the items of the VOC and the future trend of the condition to remain the same or basically the same, it should provide companies and QFD users with a forward approach to estimate and listen to the voice of the customer in the future.

Results in the illustrative example suggested that forecasting techniques are a good solution for the company to project customer preferences into the future. As far as the effort used in the QFD process is concerned, the same HOQ can be used, although the importance of each customer need might have changed over time, and new requirements associated with innovation or technology improvement may be added. Therefore, adopting the proposed approach in the traditional QFD process is worthwhile and should not incur much extra effort, particularly after taking the consequent benefits into account, that is, enabling companies to plan products that are expected to meet the future needs of customers.

The above method is appropriate only when there are sufficient historical data, which may not be the case for many companies. Trend analysis can be used to help QFD users listen to the voice of the customer in the future quantitatively, even without historical data. In fact, when designing a new product, we may not have sufficient data, and past products can be used in forecasting the needs for new products as well.

To deal with subjective information involved in the trend of importance for each VOC, fuzzy numbers were proposed to quantify vague information. Developed by Zadeh (1965), fuzzy set theory has been successfully used for the transition from vagueness to quantification in many applications, and this can easily be modified in analyzing the trend of importance of customer needs. Yet it must be noted that for both proposed methods, cautions should be taken when interpreting and utilizing the estimates of future importance values, as they are always associated with uncertainties.

Chapter 4

Variability Analysis in QFD

Traditionally, the absolute importance of the engineering characteristics is used in QFD analysis. VOCs and their importance can be obtained through surveys and investigations of the market. This is a practical way to obtain information from the customer. With such data, we have not only the mean importance, but also the variations of the importance since not all customers have the same priority. Customer variation in needs and requirements is a subject that has received less attention.

It is useful in QFD analysis to incorporate the variability of VOC and study the effect of it when it is translated into engineering characteristics. In the traditional analysis of QFD, variations are not taken into consideration although they may affect the accuracy of the final ranking of engineering characteristics. More important engineering characteristics may become less critical if their variations are different. Less important engineering characteristics may also become crucial ones. Therefore, variation analysis is useful for the decision makers to make correct selections of the most crucial engineering characteristics.

Our studies have shown that the *variations of importance of VOC may have a significant impact on the precision of the final identification*. Thus, serious attention should be given to variation analysis in QFD. The decision maker should look at not only the absolute ranking of the engineering characteristics, but also the variations, in order to make correct decisions.

In fact, variability in the results is affected by uncertainties from different sources. The variability of the requirements for different customers and the uncertainty in the correlation matrix are important sources. This chapter presents discussion and methods that can be used to incorporate variability studies into QFD.

THE NEED FOR VARIABILITY ANALYSIS IN QFD

The variability of a set of observations is an important feature in that variability measure's spread or dispersion. Practically every set of quantitative data is characterized by its variation that indicates differences among individual units. An average value would have limited significance if the variation were so great that there was no pronounced central tendency. The average becomes increasingly meaningful with a decrease in the degree of variation (Xie et al., 1998).

In traditional QFD analysis, the average importance of the engineering characteristics obtained from surveys and investigations is usually used. However, decision making based only on the mean importance may not give sufficient analytical information, or may even lead to wrong conclusions if variation is not taken into consideration. The deviation is related to sample size in the survey and other factors, which are usually not considered in the QFD analysis. In the study presented in this chapter, one assumption is that all the variations are obtained through data with equal sample sizes.

In the HOQ, if one engineering characteristic is more important than another one based on the mean values, the difference may not be significant if the variation of the first engineering characteristic is much larger than the second one. To a certain extent, it might lead us in a wrong direction by identifying the engineering characteristics with large mean importance and large deviations as crucial items. Less important items may be equally significant if their deviations are very small. Identification based only on the mean importance may not be appropriate if this happens.

Take Figure 4.1 as an illustrative case. There are two engineering characteristics with X1 and X2 as the mean importance of engineering characteristic 1 (EC1) and engineering characteristic 2 (EC2), respectively. If mean value is the only criterion, from the figure we can easily identify EC2 as being more important than EC1.

According to the empirical rule, if a data set has an approximately bell-shaped distribution, approximately 68 percent of the measurements will lie within one standard deviation of their mean, and approximately 95 percent of the measurements will lie within two standard deviations. Consequently, although EC2 is relatively crucial according to its mean, it has a weak central tendency, which leads to the interpretation that not all the customers take it as very important. There is still a large proportion of the customers who think that it is important or unimportant. On the other hand, a large portion of the data in EC1 lies within one standard deviation of EC2 with a

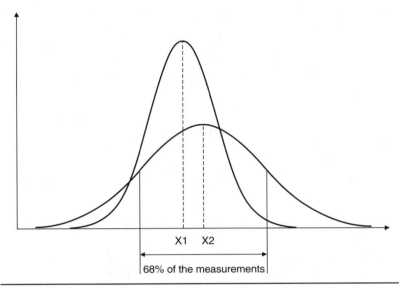

X1 X2

68% of the measurements

Figure 4.1 Less important one (X1) has a smaller standard deviation.

strong central tendency. Since almost all of the customers take EC1 as being relatively important, EC1 might be relatively crucial. The same conclusion, on the other hand, can be drawn if we consider a given degree of confidence interval in a normally distributed data set.

In ideal cases, important items of engineering characteristics should show a high degree of consistency in the judgments made by respondents, which is reflected in the relatively low standard deviations. However, even in this situation, it might be dangerous to take less-important items as not very significant.

Take Figure 4.2 as another example. EC2 that has a mean of X2 is more important than EC1 with a mean of X1, if we were to go by their mean values. However, because of the difference in central tendency, EC1 may be as crucial if we consider the upper 90th percentile. From a quality point of view, although the mean importance of EC1 is not very large, people have different opinions on its significance. A certain number of people still think that it is very important, although others think it is not very important. Items like this require consideration, especially when two means are close to each other.

One of QFD's key features is its customer-based technical design. Accurate customer information is needed in order to meet QFD's goal of satisfying customers. It is often difficult to obtain precise customer requirements

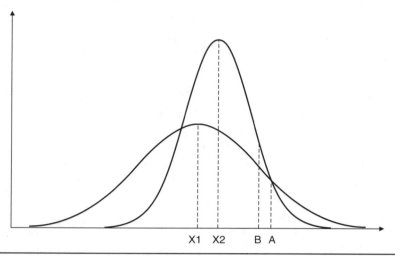

Figure 4.2   Less important item has larger standard deviation (A: 90 percent for EC1 with mean X1 and B: 90 percent for EC2 with mean X2).

because of resources, time, and technical constraints. When surveys and investigations have been carried out, it would be a waste of information if variations were not used to do a better analysis, since not using variations may lead to serious problems in the final identification of the important elements of the customer requirements.

VARIABILITY ANALYSIS OF ENGINEERING CHARACTERISTICS IN QFD

The Variations of Engineering Characteristics

In QFD analysis, for an HOQ with m engineering characteristic and n items of VOCs, the absolute weight of the jth engineering characteristic is computed as

$$a_j = \sum_{i=1}^{n} R_{ij}c_i, j = 1, ..., m \tag{4.1}$$

where a_j is the row vector of absolute weights for the engineering characteristics ($j = 1, ..., m$), R_{ij} is the weights assigned to the relationship matrix ($i = 1, ..., n; j = 1, ..., m$) and c_i is the column vector of degree of importance for the VOC items ($i = 1, ..., n$)

When a series of VOC data are obtained from the survey, the corresponding mean importance and standard deviation of the engineering characteristics can be easily deduced through their relationships above. For discrete sample data (normally, the surveyed importance of VOCs is discrete in nature), we have that

$$\bar{x} = \sum_i x_i p(x_i)$$

(4.2)

and

$$s^2 = \sum_i (x_i - \bar{x})^2 p(x_i)$$

(4.3)

Suppose there is an equal sample size, l, for each VOC item. For the ith VOC item, we can thus get one set of sample data, $c_{i1}, c_{i2}, c_{i3}, ..., c_{ix}, ..., c_{il}$. The mean importance and variance for the jth engineering characteristic are then derived as,

$$\bar{a}_j = \sum_{x=1}^{l} [a_{jx} p(a_{jx})] = \sum_{x=1}^{l} \left[\left(\sum_{i=1}^{n} R_{ij} c_{ix} \right) p \left(\sum_{i=1}^{n} R_{ij} c_{ix} \right) \right]$$

(4.4)

and

$$s_j^2 = \sum_{x=1}^{l} [(a_{jx} - \bar{a}_j)^2 p(a_{jx})] = \sum_{x=1}^{n} \left[\left(\sum_{i=1}^{n} R_{ij} c_{ix} - \bar{a}_j \right)^2 p \left(\sum_{i=1}^{n} R_{ij} c_{ix} \right) \right]$$

(4.5)

On the other hand, if there is a sufficient number of random measurements, and all of the items in the VOC voice are independent of each other, we can then consider the importance data of the VOC as being normally distributed with no covariance.

According to the sample distribution of sums, if the standard deviation for the ith VOC item is s_i, the variance for the jth engineering characteristic is

$$s_j'^2 = R_{1j}^2 s_1^2 + R_{2j}^2 s_2^2 + \cdots R_{ij}^2 s_i^2 + \cdots R_{nj}^2 s_n^2$$

(4.6)

if there are n items of VOC, and R_{ij} is the relationship between the ith VOC item and the jth engineering characteristic. The standard deviation for the jth engineering characteristic is $s_j' = \sqrt{s_j'^2}$.

In this way, the standard deviation for the VOC items could be successfully linked to those for the engineering characteristics. The standard deviations for the engineering characteristics can then be used to make further analyses and identification of the important engineering characteristics in QFD.

Variability Analysis of Engineering Characteristics

With the complete data, we can even ask the question of whether there is a significant difference between the means. An F-test can be used to check for significant differences in the treatment means (where we consider each engineering characteristic as one treatment). Practically in QFD, there should be a significant difference in the mean importance of the engineering characteristics in order that the more important ones may be accorded special consideration. Once differences amongst the mean importance have been detected in an analysis of variance (ANOVA), comparisons between the means together with the final ranking of the QFD engineering characteristics become an important task.

There are a number of procedures for comparing and ranking a group of treatment means. A popular method, known as Tukey's method, utilizes a so-called Studentized range. Tukey's (1949) procedure selects a critical distance, ω, so that the probability of making one or more Type I errors (concluding that a difference exists between a pair of treatment means when they are, in fact, identical) is α. Therefore, the risk of making a Type I error applies to the whole procedure, that is, to the comparisons of all pairs of means in the experiment, rather than to a single comparison.

Tukey's procedure relies on the assumption that the p sample means are based on independent random samples, each containing an equal number n_1 of observations. If $s = \sqrt{MSE}$ is the computed standard deviation for the analysis, the distance ω is

$$\omega = q(p, v)\frac{s}{\sqrt{n_1}} \tag{4.7}$$

where p is the number of sample means and s is the mean square error (MSE), v is the number of degrees of freedom associated with MSE, n_1 is the number of observations in each of the p samples, and $q_\alpha(p,v)$ is the critical value of the Studentized range.

The constraint for Tukey's multiple comparison procedure is that it requires the sample sizes associated with the treatments to be equal. When applied to unequal sample sizes, the procedure has been found to be conservative, that is, less likely to detect differences when they exist. Alternative methods, however, can be used to deal with unequal sample sizes.

The ranking of treatment means can be obtained according to the pairwise comparison calculations above. The pairs of engineering characteristics without significant difference can be considered identical. Whereas there may be cases where no statistical difference exists between the ith engineering characteristic and the jth engineering characteristic ($\mu_i = \mu_j$), and between the jth and the tth ($\mu_j = \mu_t$), there is a difference between the ith

and the tth ($\mu_i > \mu_t$). A range ranking of the jth engineering characteristic, if this happens, is proposed in this study.

Suppose r_i is the ranking position of the ith engineering characteristic, and r_t is the ranking position of the tth engineering characteristic. Then the jth engineering characteristic can be assigned a ranking range between the two:

$$r_j = \left[r_t, r_i \right]$$

Assumptions in the Analysis of Variance

An assumption behind the ANOVA is that the data for the treatments must come from normal probability distributions with equal variances. Checking on the ANOVA assumptions can be performed by examining the residuals. In most business applications, the assumptions will not be satisfied exactly. The ANOVA procedures are flexible, however, in the sense that slight departures from the assumptions will not significantly affect the analysis or the validity of the resulting inferences, although gross violations of the assumptions will cast doubt on the validity of the inferences.

Although nonparametric tests are normally used for ordinal data (the importance of customer requirements is normally ordinal-type data), parametric tests such as the F-test are sometimes employed on ordinal-type data. Empirical tests prove that the assumptions of parametric tests hold up well even though actual conditions depart substantially from those theoretically required. Therefore, it is common to find such tests being used in circumstances where, under a strict interpretation, only nonparametric tests are appropriate. Another reason for applying the Tukey method to variability analysis of the engineering characteristics is that by using this method, the Tukey critical distance can be obtained and used to measure the difference between pairs of engineering characteristics. A final ranking, which is needed for the QFD analysis, can thus be obtained.

In QFD analysis, if enough sample data can be obtained from customer surveys, the assumptions for ANOVA analysis can be roughly satisfied. With the emphasis on the final ranking of the engineering characteristics, slight deviation from the assumptions may be tolerated and rough analysis can be accepted.

AN APPLICATION EXAMPLE

A project was carried out that used the Internet as a case study for defining, measuring, and finally improving Internet access quality. An HOQ was built to link technical supports with VOCs and for further recommendations. This is shown in Figure 4.3 together with the degree of importance and standard deviations for the VOC items.

The absolute importance and the importance ranking of the VOCs can be easily obtained after a series of calculations. The standard deviation for the engineering characteristics, on the other hand, can be achieved following the procedures proposed in the previous part.

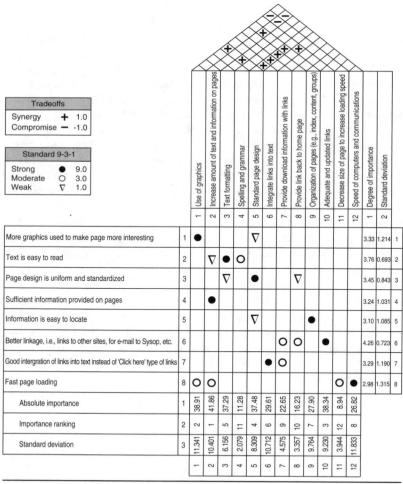

Figure 4.3 The HOQ of the case study.

ANOVAs and Tukey pair-wise comparisons were conducted on the sample data and the results are shown in Tables 4.1 and 4.2.

The columns and rows in the Tukey 95 percent confidence interval tables are labelled by their engineering characteristics. For example, the Tukey interval for the difference between the mean for Adequate (μ_1) and Decrease (μ_2) is $22.487 \leq \mu_1 - \mu_2 \leq 33.472$. The interval does not contain 0, indicating a difference.

On the other hand, the crucial distance ω is:

$$\omega = q(p, v)\frac{s}{\sqrt{n_1}} = 4.62\left(\frac{\sqrt{MSE}}{\sqrt{n_1}}\right) = 4.62\frac{\sqrt{69.3}}{\sqrt{49}} = 5.49$$

Any pair of mean difference greater than this value is considered different.

The corresponding sequence of the engineering characteristics is then:

Adequate links = Increase amount of information = Standard page design = Text formatting = Use of graphics > Integrate links into text = Organization of pages > Speed of computer > Provide download information > Provide link back to home pages > Spelling and grammar > Decrease size of pages

The equalities above mean that the items are statistically equally important. Greater than and smaller than are the indicators of statistical difference.

As a result, new rankings of the engineering characteristics can be obtained (see Table 4.3). Compared with ranking according to the mean values, the first five most important engineering characteristics can actually be regarded as equally important by considering not only their means, but also their standard deviations. Therefore, although we will still end up with the same list if we specify using the top ten items, things can be different if we specify using the top three items based on the new ranking.

Table 4.1 Analysis of variance table.

Source	DF	SS	MS	F	P
Engineering characteristics	11	68467.6	6224.3	89.87	0.000
Error	576	39893.8	69.3		
Total	587	108361.5			

Table 4.2 Tukey confidence interval.

	Adequate links	Decrease size of pages	Provide download information	Increase amount of information	Integrate links into text	Organization of pages	Provide link back to home pages	Speed of computers	Spelling and grammar	Standard page design	Text formatting
Decrease size of pages	22.487 33.472										
Provide download information	9.262 20.248	-18.717 -7.732									
Increase amount of information	-10.472 0.513	-38.452 -27.466	-25.227 -14.242								
Integrate links into text	1.854 12.840	-26.125 -15.140	-12.901 -1.915	6.834 17.819							
Organization of pages	3.507 14.493	-24.472 -13.487	-11.248 -0.262	8.487 19.472	-3.840 7.146						
Provide link back to home pages	15.671 26.656	-12.309 -1.324	0.915 11.901	20.650 31.636	8.324 19.309	6.671 17.656					
Speed of computers	4.609 15.595	-23.370 -12.385	-10.146 0.840	9.589 20.574	-2.738 8.248	-4.391 6.595	-16.554 -5.569				
Spelling and grammar	20.160 31.146	-7.819 3.166	5.405 16.391	25.140 36.125	12.813 23.799	11.160 22.146	-1.003 9.982	10.058 21.044			
Standard page design	-6.044 4.942	-34.023 -23.038	-20.799 -9.813	-1.064 9.921	-13.391 -2.405	-15.044 -4.058	-27.207 -16.222	-16.146 -5.160	-31.697 -20.711		
Text formatting	-5.819 5.166	-33.799 -22.813	-20.574 -9.589	-0.840 10.146	-13.166 -2.181	-14.819 -3.834	-26.982 -15.997	-15.921 -4.936	-31.472 -20.487	-5.268 5.717	
Use of graphics	-7.452 3.534	-35.431 -24.446	-22.207 -11.222	-2.472 8.513	-14.799 -3.813	-16.452 -5.466	-28.615 -17.630	-17.554 -6.569	-33.105 -22.120	-6.901 4.085	-7.125 3.860

According to the ranking of the means themselves (the third column of Table 4.3), the first three items in Table 4.3 should be selected. However, if standard deviations were also considered, there is in fact no statistical difference for the first five items. Special care, in this case, should be taken, and further analysis should be done.

The plots of residuals in this case show that although the assumptions of ANOVA are not perfectly satisfied, rough analysis can still be conducted. In practice, on the other hand, a large enough sample size should be used to meet the requirements and make the analysis robust.

SENSITIVITY STUDY OF VOC

In almost all the papers related to QFD, the construction of the HOQ and the preliminary analysis of customer needs are the main focus. Because the main advantage of an HOQ is its focus on customer needs and requirements, it is important to identify the customer requirements and their relative importance correctly and accurately. Generally, the relative importance of each VOC should be obtained directly from the customers. However, this

Table 4.3 Ranking comparison.

	Absolute importance	Importance ranking (according to mean)	Standard deviation	New ranking
Increase amount of text and information on pages	41.86	1	10.401	1
Use of graphics	38.91	2	11.341	1
Adequate and updated links	38.34	3	9.230	1
Standard page design	37.48	4	8.309	1
Text formatting	37.29	5	6.156	1
Integrate links into text	29.61	6	10.712	6
Organization of pages	27.90	7	9.764	6
Speed of computers and communications	26.62	8	11.833	[6–9]
Provide download information with links	22.65	9	4.575	9
Provide link back to home page	16.23	10	3.357	10
Spelling and grammar	11.28	11	2.079	[10–12]
Decrease size of page to increase loading speed	8.94	12	3.944	12

is not easy because this requires extensive survey and research, which can be costly and time consuming. It may even prove impossible in some cases.

An innovative approach to obtain the weightings of VOCs has been suggested by Akao (1990) and by Aswad (1989) involving the use of the Analytic Hierarchy Process (AHP). The AHP was originated by Saaty (1980) and it is an analytical tool, supported by simple mathematics, that enables people to explicitly rank tangible and intangible factors. Armacost et al. (1994) and Doukas et al. (1995) used the AHP method to identify and prioritize VOCs. It was suggested in Goh et al. (1995) that AHP can be used to provide better prioritization, while using QFD as a preliminary selection for important factors.

As mentioned, an attractive feature of QFD is its focus on the VOC. This process is driven by what the customers want and not solely by technology or a designer's creativity. Failing to meet customer expectations increases customer dissatisfaction and the company may, in the short term, lose orders and in the long term lose its market share. Hence, it is important for decision makers to determine their customers' needs and requirements accurately in order to optimize the use of limited resources. Since it is important to obtain an accurate understanding of customer needs for a proper use of the HOQ, sensitivity analysis of the VOCs is of great interest. If the prioritization of engineering characteristics is very sensitive to the weightings of the VOCs, the weightings would have to be accurately determined and this might justify additional resources for the determination. On the other hand, if the sensitivity is low, the focus could be on other less costly issues.

An approach to carry out sensitivity analysis of the VOCs using AHP is presented next using a published HOQ example. Results from this and similar studies indicate that prioritization based on the HOQ is not very sensitive to a small change of the weightings of customer needs. An explanation could be that the weightings commonly used in correlation metrics are discrete in nature and a change of the level of the relationship could influence the result of prioritization more than a small change of the importance of the VOC items.

Analytic Hierarchy Process

AHP is a decision-making technique. It provides a comprehensive framework for making multicriteria decisions by organizing problems into a hierarchical structure. It is a systematic procedure for representing the elements of any problem, hierarchically. It organizes the basic rationality by decomposing a general decision problem in a hierarchical fashion into subproblems that can be easily comprehended and evaluated; determining the priorities of the elements at each level of the decision hierarchy through a series of pair-wise comparison judgments to express the relative strength or intensity of impact of each element in the hierarchy; and synthesizing the priorities to determine the overall priorities of the decision alternatives.

Alternative Rankings

In AHP, common numerical values used are 1 to 9, with 1, 3, 5, 7, and 9 expressing the preferences between options as equally, moderately, strongly, very strongly, or extremely preferred, and 2, 4, 6, and 8 as intermediate values. Each pair-wise comparison represents an estimate of the ratio of the priorities or weightings of the compared elements. Applying

Saaty's eigenvector method to these data, estimates of the weightings are calculated for each pair-wise comparison matrix and for each level of the hierarchy. The eigenvector, on the other hand, provides the priority orderings. In mathematical terms the principle eigenvector is computed, and when normalized, becomes the vector of priorities.

The fundamental scale for AHP pair-wise comparison is shown in Table 4.4. (Saaty, 1980).

Table 4.4 The fundamental scale for AHP pair-wise comparison.

Intensity of importance	Definition	Explanation
1	Equal importance	Two activities contribute equally to the objective
3	Moderate importance	Experience and judgment slightly favor one activity over another
5	Strong importance	Experience and judgment strongly favor one activity over another
7	Very strong or demonstrated importance	An activity is strongly favored and its dominance demonstrated in practice
9	Extreme importance	The evidence favoring one activity over another is of the highest possible order of affirmation
2, 4, 6, 8	Intermediate value between the two adjacent judgments	When compromise is needed
Reciprocals of above nonzero numbers	If activity i has one of the above nonzero numbers assigned to it when compared with activity j, then j has the reciprocal when compared with i	

The Main Operational Steps of AHP

A brief description of the AHP operational steps is as follows:

1. Define the problem.

2. Structure a hierarchy representing the problem. Arrange goals, attributes, criteria, subcriteria, issues, activities, alternatives, and so on, in a hierarchy.

3. Perform pair-wise comparison judgments on elements at each level of the hierarchy with respect to another element higher up the hierarchy. This process produces a series of pair-wise comparison matrices at each level of the hierarchy.

4. Compute the local weightings of the elements at each level with respect to an element higher up the hierarchy.

5. Use hierarchical composition to combine the weightings to obtain the global weightings for the alternatives.

6. Check the model and repeat any part as required.

The Structure of AHP Hierarchy

Saaty applied a "functional" hierarchy to multiattribute decision problems. He stated it as follows (Saaty 1982, p. 28):

> The Top level, called the "focus," consists of only one element—the broad, overall objective. Subsequent levels may each have several elements, although their number is very small—between 5 and 9. Because the elements in one level are to be compared with one another against a criterion in the next higher level, the elements in each level must be of the same order of magnitude.

Figure 4.4 shows the structure of the AHP hierarchy analysis. The focus/objective of the decision problem is presented at the top level of the hierarchy. The second level consists of attributes identified as important in achieving the overall objective. Subsequent levels are created by dividing attributes into subattributes, subattributes into subattributes, and so on.

It is important to note that the selected attributes and subattributes should be independent to make for effective AHP analysis. The calculations in the AHP are based on the principle that the elements on a single level of the hierarchy are independent, and that their relative importance does not depend on the elements at the next lower level of the hierarchy. Thus, independence should be assured before carrying out the AHP analysis. For

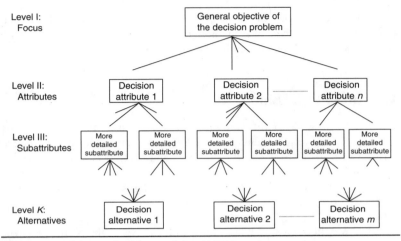

Level I: Focus		General objective of the decision problem		

Level II: Attributes	Decision attribute 1	Decision attribute 2	Decision attribute *n*

Level III: Subattributes	More detailed subattribute	More detailed subattribute	More detailed subattribute	More detailed subattribute	More detailed subattribute	More detailed subattribute

Level *K*: Alternatives	Decision alternative 1	Decision alternative 2	Decision alternative *m*

Figure 4.4 The standard form of the AHP hierarchy.

those items that are not independent, other methods, such as dividing the dependent items into several independent parts can be used.

Consistency Ratio

An important concern in using AHP is the consistency. If A is twice as important as B and B is three times as important as C, then A should be six times as important as C. Otherwise, the judgment is considered to be inconsistent. The eigenvector method permits a quantitative assessment of consistency. Saaty (1980) introduced the Consistency Ratio (CR) as an index to indicate the degree of inconsistency of judgments in a decision matrix. CR compares the inconsistency of the judgments in a decision matrix with what would have been if the decision matrix contained random judgments.

For a given decision matrix of size N, CR can be defined as

$$CR = \frac{CI}{RI} \qquad (4.8)$$

and

$$CI = \frac{\lambda_{\max} - N}{N - 1} \qquad (4.9)$$

where

CI = consistency index of the decision matrix
RI = random index of the decision matrix
$\lambda_{\max}$ = maximum eigenvalue for the decision matrix
N = number of rows (or columns) of the decision matrix

The random index of a matrix of size N was approximated by Saaty (based on large numbers of simulation runs) as partially shown in Table 4.5. In general, the consistency ratio should be less than 0.10 for acceptable results.

Weighting VOC Using AHP

The AHP with some modification is used here to assess the relative importance of quality requirements in the HOQ. An example for a hypothetical writing instrument by Wasserman (1993) and Shillito (1994) is shown in Figure 4.5.

To obtain the weightings of the VOCs using AHP, we first obtain the pair-wise comparisons of the VOCs. For illustration, the values in Table 4.6a are used.

The weight of each VOC is then calculated. According to the pair-wise comparisons in Table 4.6a, and by using an AHP software, we can get the relative importance values for the VOCs. The results are shown also in Table 4.6a. In this case, the inconsistency ratio, a measure of the consistency of pair-wise comparison, is 0.0, which indicates that the results are acceptable.

Using the results of AHP as the weightings of VOC and multiplying them with the relationships in the HOQ, we can get the relative weighting of each engineering characteristic, as shown in Table 4.6b. Comparing these results with the original HOQ in Figure 4.5, we can see that even though the relative importance of each engineering characteristic by using the AHP is different from the original HOQ, the ranking is the same.

A Sensitivity Analysis of the VOC

As mentioned in the early part of this chapter, it is difficult to obtain VOCs and the weightings of VOCs accurately in practice, and it is of great interest to study the sensitivity of the VOCs. An approach to carry out sensitivity analysis is thus developed and presented in this section. In order to

Table 4.5   Random index (RI) for matrix of size N.

RI	1	2	3	4	5	6	7	8	9	10	11
N	0.00	0.00	0.58	0.90	1.12	1.24	1.32	1.41	1.45	1.49	1.51

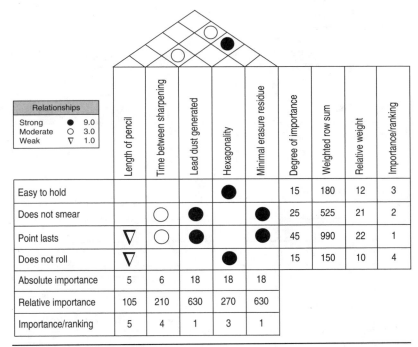

Figure 4.5 The HOQ for the example (adapted from Wasserman, 1993).

conduct the sensitivity analysis of the VOCs, we slightly increase or decrease the pair-wise comparison results of the VOCs in the AHP, and hence obtain a new ranking of the engineering characteristics. The results are then compared with the original figures to observe sensitivity. The steps in the calculation are similar to the previous section and any AHP software can be used for this purpose.

Each pair-wise comparison result increased by one unit. When the ratio of pair-wise comparison is changed, which indicates a difference in preference among customer requirements, the result of the AHP calculation may change and it might change the final result of the HOQ prioritization.

Let the ratio of each pair-wise comparison be increased by one unit. This means that if a factor, A, compared with another factor, B, was equally (moderately, strongly, and so on) preferred, it now becomes moderately (strongly, very strongly, and so on) preferred.

In other words, if the original comparison result was 1, it now becomes 2. And if the original comparison result was 2, it is now 3, and so on.

Table 4.6a   Pair-wise comparison of VOCs.

	Easy to hold	Does not smear	Point lasts	Does not roll
Easy to hold	1	1/2	1/3	1
Does not smear	2	1	1/2	2
Point lasts	3	2	1	3
Does not roll	1	1/2	1/3	1
Weightings with AHP method	0.141	0.263	0.455	0.141

Table 4.6b   The results based on the weightings in Table 4.6a.

	Length of pencil	Time between sharpening	Lead dust generated	Hexagonality	Minimal erasure residue
Absolute importance	5	6	18	18	18
Relative importance	1.019	2.154	6.462	2.538	6.462
Importance/ ranking	5	4	1	3	1

Because of the relative scale, if the original comparison result was 1/3, it becomes 1/2, and so on. The comparisons of the VOCs are shown in Table 4.7a. The weighting of each VOC can then be calculated. The relative importance for VOCs is also shown in Table 4.7a. Note that in this case, the inconsistency ratio can be computed to be 0.02, which is still considered acceptable.

Next, we use the results of the AHP method as the weightings of VOCs in the HOQ to obtain the weighting of each engineering characteristic. The weightings and final ranking of the engineering characteristics are shown in Table 4.7b.

From the analysis, we can see that even though the relative importance for each engineering characteristic is different from the results obtained earlier, the change is small. In this particular case, the ranking of the engineering characteristics is the same, so that the prioritization remains unchanged. Thus, in this case, the HOQ is not sensitive to changes of the weightings of

Table 4.7a   Pair-wise comparison of VOCs.

	Easy to hold	Does not smear	Point lasts	Does not roll
Easy to hold	1	1	1/2	2
Does not smear	1	1	1	3
Point lasts	2	1	1	4
Does not roll	1/2	1/3	1/4	1
Weightings with AHP method	0.225	0.297	0.377	0.100

Table 4.7b   The results based on the weightings in Table 4.7a.

	Length of pencil	Time between sharpening	Lead dust generated	Hexagonality	Minimal erasure residue
Absolute importance	5	6	18	18	18
Relative importance	1.152	2.022	6.066	2.925	6.066
Importance/ ranking	5	4	1	3	1

VOCs, and the analyst can rely on the HOQ for prioritization even if the information from the customers regarding their needs is very limited.

Each pair-wise comparison result reduced by one unit. This time, the results of the pair-wise comparison are reduced by one. This means that the preference is weakened by one unit. The results of VOC comparisons are shown in Table 4.8a. We also calculate the weighting of each VOC, and obtain the relative importance for each VOC item. The results of the weightings are shown in Table 4.8a (the inconsistency ratio is 0.02, which is acceptable).

The results of the AHP can next be used as the weightings of VOCs in the HOQ, and the relative weighting for each engineering characteristic can be obtained. The results are shown in Table 4.8b. Again, there is a small change regarding the actual relative importance. At the same time, the ranking of each engineering characteristic still remains the same.

Random Changes of the Pair-wise Comparison Results

In the above two subsections, systematic changes (+1 or -1) of pair-wise values of AHP have been applied, and the results show that HOQ analysis is not very sensitive to the systematic changes of the pair-wise comparison results.

To give a complete consideration of the sensitivity of HOQ for analyzing customer requirements and prioritizing technical responses, random changes of the pair-wise comparison results (some of them slightly increase, and some of them slightly decrease) are applied in this section. Of the 30 random tests shown in Table 4.10, only 3 tests changed the final ranking of

Table 4.8a   Pair-wise comparison of VOCs.

	Easy to hold	Does not smear	Point lasts	Does not roll
Easy to hold	1	1/3	1/4	—
Does not smear	3	1	1/3	1
Point lasts	4	3	1	2
Does not roll	2	1	1/2	1
Weightings with AHP method	0.097	0.216	0.476	0.211

Table 4.8b The results based on the weightings in Table 4.8a.

	Length of pencil	Time between sharpening	Lead dust generated	Hexagonality	Minimal erasure residue
Absolute importance	5	6	18	18	18
Relative importance	0.978	2.076	6.228	2.772	6.228
Importance/ ranking	5	4	1	3	1

the technical responses. The results showed that the final ranking of the technical responses remained the same for 90 percent of the time.

Table 4.9 shows the 30 random samples taken and the test results. The first column of the table contains the pair-wise comparison results of the VOC items. Slight changes (either increases or decreases) to the comparison results in the original Table 4.6a are applied. As shown in Table 4.6a, the upper-right triangle of the pair-wise comparison results and the lower-left triangle of the pair-wise comparison results are reciprocal with respect to the diagonal. All the elements in the diagonal, on the other hand, are 1. Therefore, six pair-wise comparisons are sufficient to represent all of the comparison ratios. We define them as elements (1) to (6) in Table 4.9.

Given that the pair-wise comparison results in the first column of Table 4.10 are [1, 1/2, 2, 1/3, 1, 2], this means that the first element in Table 4.9 is 1 (meaning "Easy to hold" is equally important as "Does not smear"), the second element in Table 4.9 is 1/2 (meaning "Easy to hold" is 50 percent as important as "Point lasts"), and so on.

The second column of Table 4.10 shows the weightings of the four VOC items in the same sequence as those in Table 4.6a. The third column and the fourth column show the weightings and the rankings of the technical responses in the same sequence as those in Table 4.6b. The bold numbers in the last column of Table 4.10 are those rankings that have changed during the random increases or decreases of the pair-wise comparison results.

The random tests in this section substantiate that the QFD prioritization in this example is not very sensitive to small changes of the pair-wise comparison ratios.

Table 4.9   Elements of the pair-wise comparisons of VOCs.

	Easy to hold	Does not smear	Point lasts	Does not roll
Easy to hold		(1)	(2)	(3)
Does not smear			(4)	(5)
Point lasts				(6)
Does not roll				

Reverse Each Pair-wise Comparison Result

The next step is to reverse the pair-wise comparisons, resulting in less important needs becoming more important ones instead. Thus, if Factor A is preferred to Factor B, Factor B now becomes preferred instead. In this case, we should expect a change of the ranking, because the HOQ would otherwise be too insensitive to the VOC changes.

In the AHP, this change means that if the original comparison result was 2, it becomes 1/2, and if the original comparison result was 1/2, it becomes 2, and so on. The weighting of each VOC can then be calculated as before. To save lines, we omit the steps of getting the weighting of each VOC, as the procedures are in fact the same as the previous two situations. Instead, we show only the final result of the ranking of the engineering characteristics in the HOQ in Table 4.11.

DISCUSSION

The HOQ is the primary planning tool used in QFD for translating customer requirements into design requirements to meet customer needs. Since QFD concentrates on customer expectations, sensitivity analysis of the VOCs is important.

The illustrative example shows that *with respect to small changes in the weightings of VOCs, QFD is a rather robust method for the prioritization of process and product design factors*. Therefore, in practice, when HOQ is used, the analyst could be assured of a reasonable prioritization even if the weightings of customer requirements are not with 100 percent precision and certainty. On the other hand, for a specific application when

Table 4.10   Random changes of the pair-wise comparison results.

The pair-wise comparisons of the VOCs	Weightings of VOCs by AHP	Weightings of the technical responses	Rankings of the technical responses
[1, 1/2, 2, 1/3, 1, 2]	[0.23, 0.18, 0.43, 0.16]	[1.29, 1.81, 5.43, 3.57, 5.43]	[5, 4, 1, 3, 1]
[1, 1/2, 1/2, 1, 1, 2]	[0.17, 0.24, 0.34, 0.24]	[1.10, 1.76, 5.27, 3.74, 5.27]	[5, 4, 1, 3, 1]
[1, 1/2, 1/2, 1/3, 3, 2]	[0.16, 0.25, 0.42, 0.18]	[1.08, 1.99, 5.96, 3.05, 5.96]	[5, 4, 1, 3, 1]
[1, 1/2, 1/2, 1/3, 1, 4]	[0.16, 0.16, 0.49, 0.19]	[1.15, 1.96, 5.87, 3.21, 5.87]	[5, 4, 1, 3, 1]
[1, 1/4, 2, 1, 1, 2]	[0.20, 0.23, 0.41, 0.16]	[1.17, 1.92, 5.76, 3.25, 5.76]	[5, 4, 1, 3, 1]
[1, 1/4, 2, 1/3, 3, 2]	[0.18, 0.22, 0.49, 0.12]	[1.14, 2.10, 6.31, 2.70, 6.31]	[5, 4, 1, 3, 1]
[1, 1/4, 2, 1/3, 1, 4]	[0.18, 0.16, 0.54, 0.12]	[1.20, 2.10, 6.31, 2.70, 6.31]	[5, 4, 1, 3, 1]
[1, 1/4, 1/2, 1, 3, 2]	[0.15, 0.31, 0.37, 0.17]	[0.98, 2.04, 6.13, 2.87, 6.13]	[5, 4, 1, 3, 1]
[1, 1/4, 1/2, 1, 1, 4]	[0.13, 0.23, 0.45, 0.18]	[1.03, 2.05, 6.16, 2.84, 6.16]	[5, 4, 1, 3, 1]
[1, 1/4, 1/2, 1/3, 3, 4]	[0.13, 0.22, 0.52, 0.14]	[1.04, 2.21, 6.62, 2.38, 6.62]	[5, 4, 1, 3, 1]
[1/3, 1/2, 2, 1, 1, 2]	[0.19, 0.32, 0.32, 0.17]	[1.05, 1.92, 5.57, 3.25, 5.75]	[5, 4, 1, 3, 1]
[1/3, 1/2, 2, 1/3, 3, 2]	[0.16, 0.29, 0.43, 0.12]	[1.03, 2.16, 6.48, 2.52, 6.48]	[5, 4, 1, 3, 1]
[1/3, 1/2, 2, 1/3, 1, 4]	[0.17, 0.24, 0.47, 0.13]	[1.11, 2.10, 6.31, 2.70, 6.31]	[5, 4, 1, 3, 1]
[1/3, 1/2, 1/2, 1, 3, 2]	[0.12, 0.39, 0.32, 0.17]	[0.86, 2.12, 6.35, 2.65, 6.35]	[5, 4, 1, 3, 1]
[1/3, 1/2, 1/2, 1, 1, 4]	[0.12, 0.29, 0.40, 0.19]	[0.95, 2.06, 6.18, 2.80, 6.18]	[5, 4, 1, 3, 1]
[1/3, 1/2, 1/2, 1/3, 3, 4]	[0.12, 0.27, 0.48, 0.13]	[0.96, 2.24, 6.73, 2.26, 6.73]	[5, 4, 1, 3, 1]
[1/3, 1/4, 1/2, 1, 3, 4]	[0.09, 0.36, 0.41, 0.13]	[0.83, 2.32, 6.95, 2.05, 6.95]	**[5, 3, 1, 4, 1]**
[1/3, 1/4, 2, 1, 3, 2]	[0.14, 0.37, 0.37, 0.12]	[0.92, 2.21, 6.63, 2.37, 6.63]	[5, 4, 1, 3, 1]
[1/3, 1/4, 2, 1, 1, 4]	[0.14, 0.29, 0.42, 0.14]	[0.99, 2.15, 6.45, 2.55, 6.45]	[5, 4, 1, 3, 1]
[1/3, 1/4, 2, 1/3, 3, 4]	[0.13, 0.26, 0.52, 0.09]	[0.99, 2.35, 7.06, 1.94, 7.06]	**[5, 3, 1, 4, 1]**
[1, 1/2, 2, 1/3, 1, 4]	[0.22, 0.17, 0.48, 0.13]	[1.13, 1.95, 5.84, 3.16, 5.84]	[5, 4, 1, 3, 1]
[1/3, 1/2, 2, 1, 3, 2]	[0.17, 0.39, 0.32, 0.12]	[0.96, 2.12, 6.35, 2.65, 6.35]	[5, 4, 1, 3, 1]
[1/3, 1/4, 1, 1/3, 3, 2]	[0.11, 0.28, 0.48, 0.14]	[0.94, 2.27, 6.80, 2.21, 6.80]	**[5, 3, 1, 4, 1]**
[1/3, 1/2, 1/2, 1/3, 1, 3]	[0.12, 0.22, 0.46, 0.19]	[1.03, 2.05, 6.15, 2.85, 6.15]	[5, 4, 1, 3, 1]
[1, 1/2, 2, 1, 3, 2]	[0.24, 0.31, 0.33, 0.13]	[1.16, 1.92, 5.75, 3.24, 5.57]	[5, 4, 1, 3, 1]
[1, 1/2, 2, 1/2, 3, 4]	[0.22, 0.24, 0.44, 0.10]	[1.19, 2.05, 6.14, 2.86, 6.14]	[5, 4, 1, 3, 1]
[1/3, 1/2, 1/2, 1/3, 1, 2]	[0.11, 0.22, 0.43, 0.24]	[1.00, 1.94, 5.83, 3.17, 5.83]	[5, 4, 1, 3, 1]
[1/3, 1/4, 1/2, 1/3, 2, 2]	[0.09, 0.25, 0.48, 0.18]	[0.93, 2.19, 6.57, 2.43, 6.57]	[5, 4, 1, 3, 1]
[1, 2, 3, 2, 4, 1]	[0.25, 0.38, 0.16, 0.12]	[1.32, 1.60, 4.81, 4.20, 4.81]	[5, 4, 1, 3, 1]
[2, 1/2, 3, 1/2, 1, 4]	[0.29, 0.16, 0.44, 0.12]	[1.42, 1.79, 5.36, 3.64, 5.36]	[5, 4, 1, 3, 1]

Table 4.11   The results when pair-wise comparison in AHP is reversed.

	Length of pencil	Time between sharpening	Lead dust generated	Hexagonality	Minimal erasure residue
Absolute importance	5	6	18	18	18
Relative importance	1.513	0.894	2.682	6.318	2.682
Importance/ranking	4	5	2	1	2

we have the HOQ, similar sensitivity analysis can be carried out and the exact sensitivity can be obtained, if needed.

It should be noted that it is not unexpected that the prioritization is not sensitive to small changes in the VOCs. This is because the relationships in the correlation matrix are discrete in nature. Changes of the relationships could in fact cause more changes in the final prioritization than small changes of the weightings of the VOC items (Shen et al., 1999).

Sensitivity study is very useful in practice, as with its use. The analyst could select to focus more on the correlation matrix than on obtaining very accurate weightings of customer requirements, which are usually costly to determine. A multilevel classification of the strengths of the correlation in the correlation matrix, such as a five level correlation classification instead of the three-level classification, could probably be used to improve the analysis in situations where additional resources are available.

Chapter 5

Prioritization and Decision Making Using QFD

After constructing the HOQ, an important task is to prioritize the technical requirements so that the process or product can be designed to better meet the needs of the customer. A simple ranking of the technical requirements may not be sufficient for the decision makers. Information may be lacking on detailed or more specific results with regard to which technical requirements to really focus on, the importance levels to be chosen, or the effects on the customer needs.

This chapter discusses several techniques that can help answer some of the above issues. Since cost is usually of great concern to management and customers, we first consider building a model that integrates various cost elements into the customer satisfaction formulation. Given a fixed budget, it is then possible to study the problem of how to allocate the budget to different technical requirements so that customer satisfaction can be maximized.

When prioritizing the technical requirements, the Analytical Hierarchy Process (AHP) method can also be adopted instead of the ranking provided by an HOQ. We investigate its uses here, and also compare it with the traditional application of HOQ. In fact, different types of information are needed for AHP compared to HOQ prioritization. Hence they are complementary rather than competing techniques.

Furthermore, we shall cover the application of design of experiment (DOE) techniques in association with QFD. This is a useful consideration because the relationship matrix in HOQ usually provides very rough information. When certain technical requirements are important, detailed analysis and more specific relationships will need to be obtained. DOE is a commonly used technique for process and product improvement.

OPTIMIZATION MODEL FOR CUSTOMER SATISFACTION

Achieving higher quality is to better meet customer requirements and exceed their expectations. However, financial and other resource constraints, such as time and manpower, limit the improvement that can be achieved. From a practical point of view, when a fixed amount of resources are available, one should try to maximize the use of them in terms of increasing customer satisfaction. In this section, some models for this type of analysis are discussed.

Integrating Optimization Techniques in QFD Analysis

QFD can be used to improve the quality of the production process. Recently, there have been discussions about ways to improve the use of QFD. However, current QFD studies have the limitation of providing an objective-based evaluation of cost tradeoffs. Companies nowadays are not only struggling to maximize customer satisfaction using a limited amount of resources, but also working for an effective distribution of these resources into the production process. In the future, organizational success will be based on focusing all strategies, decisions, and activities on maximizing customer benefit per dollar (Samson and Wacker, 1998).

When resources (such as financial budget) are limited, one has to prioritize the possible actions and examine the effectiveness of these actions. Wasserman (1993) used a cost index for resource allocation. In this section, a linear programming (LP) model based on the HOQ for the improvement of product quality is illustrated. The focus is on how the product or process can be improved based on resource distribution to each engineering characteristic and the effect of this distribution on the final goal.

An Optimization Model Based on HOQ

A practical problem when using the HOQ for product and process improvement is to decide which technical factors to change. *Because resources are always limited*, it is important to allocate time and cost in an appropriate way so that the maximum level of quality can be achieved.

Given a limited amount of financial resources for an HOQ, the following model is proposed for solving the decision problem. It is formulated as an optimization model that can be solved easily. The decision variable, objective function, and the constraints are as follows.

Decision variable:

X_j: the amount of resources distributed to the jth engineering characteristic.

Objective function:

$$Z = \text{Max} \left\{ \frac{\sum_i W_i \sum_j R_{ij}^{norm} X_j}{C_j} \right\} \qquad (5.1)$$

In the objective function, W_i is the weight of the ith VOC according to the HOQ; R_{ij}^{norm} is the normalized relationship between the ith VOC and the jth engineering characteristics, and C_j is the cost required to elevate the jth engineering characteristic to target.

Normalized relationships are commonly used in the quantitative analysis of QFD to give a better representation of the underlying relationships between the VOCs and the engineering characteristics. Because the normalized relationships proposed by Lyman (1990) are accurate only when the design requirements do not exhibit a high degree of dependence, an extension of Lyman's normalization procedure that can accommodate dependencies was then developed by Wasserman in 1993.

To model the design requirement space, it was assumed in Wasserman's study that the design requirements are spanned by the unit vector, $\{\underline{v}_k\}$, $k = 1, 2,\ldots, n$, which does not necessarily comprise an orthogonal vector basis. To represent dependencies between design requirements, the notation, γ_{jk} is introduced and it denotes the elements of $\underline{\gamma}$, the correlation matrix, describing the correlation between design requirements j and k:

$$\gamma_{jk} \equiv \underline{v}_j \cdot \underline{v}_k \qquad (5.2)$$

Thus, the transformation is

$$R_{ij}^{norm} = \frac{\sum_{k=1}^{n} R_{ik} \cdot \gamma_{kj}}{\sum_{j=1}^{n} \sum_{k=1}^{n} R_{ij} \cdot \gamma_{jk}} \qquad (5.3)$$

and R_{ij}^{norm} can be interpreted as the incremental change in the level of fulfillment of the ith VOC, as the jth engineering characteristic is fulfilled to a certain level.

It should be pointed out that other normalization methods could also be chosen for the relationship normalization. Wasserman's method is selected here because it was first applied (by Wasserman) for cost consideration in the QFD analysis.

One assumption in this model is that the VOCs are independent of each other. This applies to most cases. If there are dependencies between VOCs, several methods such as dividing the corresponding VOCs into separate parts can be used to solve the problem.

In the objective function, X_j / C_j denotes the degree of fulfillment for the jth engineering characteristic, $\sum_j R_{ij}^{norm} X_j / C_j$. This describes the impact of the fulfillment of the jth engineering characteristic on the ith VOC. Finally, $\sum W_i \sum_j R_{ij}^{norm} X_j / C_j$ represents the overall impact of the fulfillment of all the engineering characteristics on the final customer satisfaction.

Constraints

In practice, there could be a number of different constraints on the QFD optimization problem. Here, a general model that takes into account several reasonable constraints related to QFD analysis is proposed.

The first constraint is the resource allocated to the project, which is in the form of budgeted amounts of financial resources. That is,

$$\sum_j X_j \leq C \tag{5.4}$$

where C is the budget allocated to the quality improvement effort of the product concerned.

Second, customers might demand a minimum satisfaction level for a given VOC. The manufacturers might also use these satisfaction levels as minimum design requirements because of their competitive concerns. In order to incorporate satisfaction level into the QFD analysis, Chen (1997) developed a model which allows designers to achieve the aspiration levels of satisfaction for a given quality characteristic. Colton and Staples (1997) used a minimum satisfaction level to indicate the performance level above which the customer is said to be fully satisfied, and a minimum tolerance level to indicate the performance level below which the customer is said to be completely dissatisfied.

The customer satisfaction constraint we propose is:

$$\frac{W_i \sum_j R_{ij} X_j}{C_j} \geq I_i \tag{5.5}$$

where I_i is the minimum percentage of satisfaction increment required by customers for the ith VOC.

Besides the above two types of constraints, there might also be boundary conditions for the degree of fulfillment of each engineering characteristic.

Improving certain design parameters or using another type of more advanced raw material might change a given technical factor by a positive amount. However, some of the technical restrictions might also limit the amount of fulfillment that is possible by a given technical requirement. Thus, decision makers are recommended to define upper and lower limits to the fulfillment of engineering characteristics according to their own experience.

Here, we use dimensionless values in the range of [0, 1] to represent the range from basic fulfillment to complete fulfillment, which provides a weighted, dimensionless number that represents how well customer wishes are met. That is,

$$0 \le \frac{X_j}{C_j} \le 1$$

In practice, other constraints can also be added to the model if needed. The optimization model can then be adjusted to fit the new constraints. Solutions to this type of problems are straightforward and any optimization software can be used for this purpose.

One assumption of the optimization model is that the normalized relationships provide acceptable descriptions of the relationships between the degree of technical fulfillment and the degree of customer satisfaction. The normalization proposed by Wasserman (1993) does give a straightforward and reasonable way of linking these two aspects successfully. Another assumption in the model is that the unit incremental cost between basic fulfillment and complete fulfillment of the engineering characteristics needs to be constant. If this requirement cannot be met in practice, more complicated models that allow a variable unit incremental cost should be applied.

An Example

In this section, we use the example of an HOQ (see Figure 4.5 on p. 75) from an article by Wasserman (1993) to illustrate the use of the model and the proposed approach. This simple example was also used in Balthazard and Gargeya (1995) as a case study. The original example by Wasserman was for a hypothetical writing instruction. There were a total of five engineering characteristics. The decision variables and the assumed costs for complete fulfillment of the engineering characteristics are shown in Table 5.1. The normalized relationships according to the transformation by Wasserman are shown in Table 5.2.

Suppose that the budget of the company to improve the quality of the pencil is $3,000. The problem is then how to optimally distribute this amount to the various engineering characteristics so that total customer satisfaction can be optimized.

In this case, the objective function is:

$$\text{Max } Z = \frac{\sum_i W_i \sum_j R_{ij}^{norm} X_j}{C_j}$$

$$= \frac{15 \times 0.25 \times X_1}{500} + \frac{15 \times 0.75 \times X_4}{1000} + \frac{25 \times 0.19 \times X_2}{200} + \frac{25 \times 0.405 \times X_3}{700}$$

$$+ \frac{25 \times 0.405 \times X_5}{1000} + \frac{45 \times 0.023 \times X_1}{500} + \frac{45 \times 0.185 \times X_2}{200} +$$

$$+ \frac{45 \times 0.396 \times X_3}{700} + \frac{45 \times 0.396 \times X_5}{1000} + \frac{15 \times 0.1 \times X_1}{500} + \frac{15 \times 0.9 \times X_4}{1000}$$

Table 5.1 Decision variables and the cost for complete fulfillment.

Number	Engineering characteristics	Decision variable	Cost for complete fulfillment (C_j)
1	length of pencil	X_1	$500
2	time between sharpening	X_2	$200
3	lead dust generated	X_3	$700
4	hexagonality	X_4	$1,000
5	minimal erasure residue	X_5	$1,000

Table 5.2 The normalized relations in HOQ.

	Length of pencil	Time between sharpening	Lead dust generated	Hexagonality	Minimal erasure residue
Easy to hold	.250			.750	
Does not smear		.190	.405		.405
Point lasts	.023	.185	.396		.396
Does not roll	.100			.900	

The constraints are:

(1) $X_1 + X_2 + X_3 + X_4 + X_5 \leq \$3,000$

(2) Suppose the required percentages of incremental satisfaction for the customer requirements are what is shown in Table 5.3. The second type of constraint then becomes

$$\frac{15 \times 0.25 \times X_1}{500} + \frac{15 \times 0.75 \times X_4}{1000} \geq 150\%$$

$$\frac{25 \times 0.19 \times X_2}{200} + \frac{25 \times 0.405 \times X_3}{700} + \frac{25 \times 0.405 \times X_5}{1000} \geq 200\%$$

$$\frac{45 \times 0.023 \times X_1}{500} + \frac{45 \times 0.185 \times X_2}{200} +$$
$$\frac{45 \times 0.396 \times X_3}{700} + \frac{45 \times 0.396 \times X_5}{1000} \geq 150\%$$

$$\frac{15 \times 0.1 \times X_1}{500} + \frac{15 \times 0.9 \times X_4}{1000} \geq 150\%$$

(3) For each engineering characteristic, we might have a range for its degree of fulfillment. The following constraints are assumed:

$$0 \leq \frac{X_1}{500} \leq 1 \quad 0 \leq \frac{X_2}{200} \leq 1 \quad 0 \leq \frac{X_3}{700} \leq 1 \quad 0 \leq \frac{X_4}{1000} \leq 1 \quad 0 \leq \frac{X_5}{1000} \leq 1$$

The optimization problem can be solved using a linear software program. With the X_js as the decision variables, the results are:

$$X_1 = 300 \quad X_2 = 200 \quad X_3 = 500 \quad X_4 = 1000 \quad X_5 = 1000$$

Table 5.3 Minimum percentage of incremental satisfaction required by the customers.

VOC	Percentage of improvement required
Easy to hold	150%
Does not smear	200%
Point lasts	150%
Does not roll	150%

In Wasserman's model, the W_j / C_j ratio, representing importance to cost index, was used to prioritize the resource distribution. The top priority was to allocate the needed resources to the engineering characteristic with the highest W_j / C_j ratio. Once the first engineering characteristic is fulfilled, resources should be allocated to the next highest-ranking engineering characteristic, and so on.

In our model, instead of using the importance to cost index, LP is applied. It is not necessarily true in our model that the engineering characteristic with the highest importance to cost index is satisfied first because the cost in this study is the complete fulfillment cost, not the incremental increase in unit cost proposed by Wasserman. As shown in Table 5.4, X_3 and X_5 have the same importance. X_5 is completely fulfilled with its budget share of $1,000. However, X_3 cannot be completely fulfilled with its budget share of $500 although its cost for complete fulfillment is $700, which is relatively smaller than the cost for complete fulfillment of X_5 ($1,000). One possible reason is that the constraints and the objective function in the LP model perform differently compared with Wasserman's importance to cost ratio.

Furthermore, constraints—such as the minimum satisfaction percentages for VOCs—are considered in our model, which not only ensure that the objective of overall customer satisfaction is met, but also make the solutions more reasonable and useful.

Finally, operations research software, which is needed to solve the proposed model, is widely available and easy to apply. For large and complicated problems, this kind of existing computer software is normally considered to be a more favorable computation method than other kinds of calculations.

Some Special Cases

Sometimes, because the setup cost of each engineering characteristic is rather large, not all of the engineering characteristics can be dealt with at the same time. We might want to select only one or two of the responses to

Table 5.4   The information on the engineering characteristics.

	X_1	X_2	X_3	X_4	X_5
Budget share	300	200	500	1,000	1,000
Cost for complete fulfillment	500	200	700	1,000	1,000
Importance	4	3	1	2	1

make better use of the resources. Because our model is a general one, it is easy to deal with this type of situation. We now present the case in which we want to select only one or two engineering characteristics.

Case in Which Only One Engineering Characteristic Is To Be Selected

Suppose the objective is to use the smallest amount of financial resources possible. To save resources, we have to select the smallest complete fulfillment cost from all possible C_js. Suppose that this is Cs (the complete fulfillment cost of the sth engineering characteristic), and that the amount of financial resources distributed to this engineering characteristic is X_s. The problem is then simplified to:

Maximize

$$Z = \sum_i W_i R_{is}^{norm} \frac{X_s}{C_s} \tag{5.6}$$

subject to

$$X_s \leq C \quad \text{and} \quad 0 \leq \frac{X_s}{C_s} \leq 1 \tag{5.7}$$

We did not include the satisfaction level constraints for VOCs in this model because the major purpose here is to maximize the objective function within the limits of all technical possibilities and under budgetary constraints. Normally, not all of the VOCs can be satisfied by a single engineering characteristic. Therefore, it is not necessary to set satisfaction levels for the VOCs. If needed, they can be added to the constraints.

In our illustrative example, the second engineering characteristic has the smallest complete fulfillment cost. Suppose the amount of financial resources distributed to this engineering characteristic is X_2, and the budget is $150. Then the model is:

Maximize

$$Z = \frac{25 \times 0.19 \times X_2}{200} + \frac{45 \times 0.185 \times X_2}{200}$$

Subject to

$$(1) \qquad X_2 \leq 150 \quad \text{and} \quad 0 \leq \frac{X_2}{200} \leq 1$$

The result for X_2 is \$150, which means that all the available resources are put in to affect further quality improvement.

Case When Two Engineering Characteristics Are To Be Selected

Now suppose that we can only afford to change two engineering characteristics with the smallest fulfillment costs. The problem is now to select the two smallest complete fulfillment costs from all the C_js. Suppose they are C_s and C_k (the complete fulfillment costs of the sth engineering characteristic and the kth engineering characteristic), and the amount of financial resources distributed to these responses are X_s and X_k.

The model is then:

Maximize

$$Z = \sum_i W_i \left(R_{is}^{norm} \frac{X_s}{C_s} + R_{ik}^{norm} \frac{X_k}{C_k} \right) \tag{5.8}$$

subject to

(1) $X_s + X_k \leq C$

(2) $W_i \left(R_{is} \dfrac{X_s}{C_s} + R_{ik} \dfrac{X_k}{C_k} \right) \geq I_i$

(3) $0 \leq \dfrac{X_s}{C_s} \leq 1 \quad 0 \leq \dfrac{X_k}{C_k} \leq 1$

In this example, resources are given to the two engineering characteristics with the smallest complete fulfillment costs, which are X_1 and X_2. If the budget is \$600, with other constraints remaining the same, the LP model is then:

Maximize

$$Z = \frac{15 \times 0.25 \times X_1}{500} + \frac{45 \times 0.023 \times X_1}{500} + \frac{15 \times 0.01 \times X_1}{500} +$$

$$\frac{25 \times 0.19 \times X_2}{200} + \frac{45 \times 0.185 \times X_2}{200}$$

Subject to

(1) $X_1 + X_2 \leq 600$

(2) $\dfrac{15 \times 0.25 \times X_1}{500} \geq 150\%$

$$\frac{25 \times 0.19 \times X_2}{200} \geq 200\%$$

$$\frac{45 \times 0.023 \times X_1}{500} + \frac{45 \times 0.185 \times X_2}{200} \geq 150\%$$

$$\frac{15 \times 0.1 \times X_1}{500} \geq 150\%$$

$$(3) \qquad 0 \leq \frac{X_1}{500} \leq 1 \; ; \; 0 \leq \frac{X_2}{200} \leq 1$$

The result is that the resources distributed to X_1 and X_2 are $500 and $100 respectively.

APPLYING ANALYTICAL HIERARCHY PROCESS TECHNIQUE TO QFD

QFD is a very useful management technique in multicriteria decision making because of its simplicity and clarity. It is based on the construction and analysis of an HOQ, which documents the transformation of customer needs into the technical characteristics of a product. The prioritization matrix method is used in the HOQ to obtain the relative importance of customers' needs (Cohen, 1995).

Recently, AHP has been proposed for application to QFD to generate the relative importance of the voice of the customer. AHP is a powerful tool for problem solving and decision making in a complex environment. Instead of weighting the alternatives according to one criterion at only one level as in the prioritization matrix method (PMM), AHP structures a complex, multicriteria problem hierarchically. In fact, AHP has been used by many authors to identify and prioritize VOCs in the HOQ (Akao, 1990; Armacost et al., 1994; Aswad, 1989; Doukas et al., 1995; Fukuda et al., 1993; and Xie et al., 1995).

In this chapter, we suggest the use of the AHP method not only in the weighting of VOCs, but also during the entire prioritization process in the HOQ. We then compare the procedures of the QFD and the AHP methods and discuss their advantages and disadvantages. By considering accuracy, difficulty, time needed, costs, and other factors that may affect the use of the two methods in practice, we give some further recommendations with regard to the choice of method to employ.

Prioritization Based on HOQ

In the HOQ, the relative weights of VOCs are obtained from the customers themselves. The question of "How important is a particular need to the customer?" can be answered directly by market research. Here, the customers need not make pair-wise comparisons. They are instead asked to give each requirement a number expressing its relative importance according to their own considerations and criteria. This methodology forms the basis for using PMM in QFD.

The steps to build the HOQ using the PMM are listed below:

- List VOCs (WHATs).

- List engineering characteristic (HOWs).

- Develop a relationship matrix between the WHATs and the HOWs.

- Develop an interrelationship matrix between pairs of HOWs.

- Develop the prioritization for the VOCs.

- Develop the prioritization for the engineering characteristics.

We now use an example of HOQ to illustrate the basic structure and procedure of the HOQ. The example is based on a study on tourist attractions in Singapore (Pawitra, 1997). The HOQ is shown in Figure 5.1.

This HOQ shows that the degree of importance of the customer needs are given by the customers. The numbers assigned to the weak, medium, and strong relationships are 1, 3, and 9. By multiplying the row weights with the relationships, we can obtain the weights of the engineering characteristics. The ranking of the importance of the engineering characteristics can then be obtained.

USE OF AHP FOR PRIORITIZATION

Direct Use of the AHP Method

AHP is appealing for solving large-scale real-world problems. Prioritization in the HOQ is a complex, multicriteria decision making problem. The weight analysis of VOCs and engineering characteristics in the HOQ is cumbersome to calculate. But doing so does bring valuable information to the decision makers. The AHP method is a suitable alternative for weighting VOCs and engineering characteristics in the HOQ. Most of the research on the application of AHP to the HOQ has, in the past, been focused on using AHP to

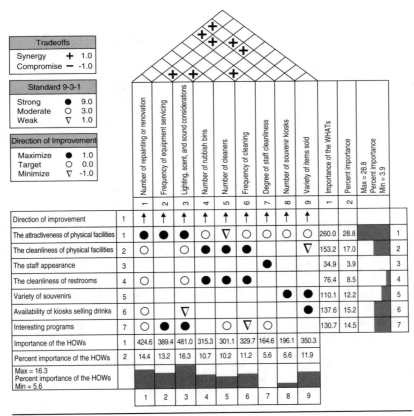

Figure 5.1 The HOQ for illustration.

weight only the VOCs. The AHP method can in fact be directly used in the prioritization of the engineering characteristics. In this manner, the overall HOQ analysis becomes more complete.

The AHP method requires that the alternatives and the criteria at the same level of the hierarchy be independent. Within the HOQ, the VOCs can be independent, but the engineering characteristics may not be independent since they may have relationships as shown in the roof of the HOQ. However, the engineering characteristics can be divided into more detailed descriptors, and with each separate part taken as a new engineering characteristic. The engineering characteristics can become independent of each other based on some appropriate adjustment. The AHP method can then be applied to the engineering characteristics. In our illustrative example later, the engineering characteristics are assumed to be independent.

Steps in Using the AHP for Prioritization

The adjusted operational steps for applying AHP to the HOQ are:

1. Define the problem.

2. Structure a hierarchy that represents the problem.

3. Perform pair-wise comparison judgments on the VOCs with respect to the goal of the HOQ.

4. Perform pair-wise comparison judgments on the engineering characteristics with respect to the VOCs.

5. Compute the local weights of the VOCs and the engineering characteristics in the hierarchy.

6. Check the model and repeat any of the above steps.

An Illustrative Example

For the example in Theresia (1997) presented in Figure 5.1, if we use AHP, the whole HOQ can be seen as a hierarchical system with three levels, which indicate focuses, attributes, and alternatives. The procedure to solve this hierarchical system by the AHP method is:

1. Make pair-wise comparisons of the VOCs with respect to the goal. The comparison results are shown in Table 5.5.

2. Make pair-wise comparisons of the alternatives with respect to the criteria in the higher level. The detailed comparison results are shown in Shen (2000).

3. Calculate the weights of the criteria and the alternatives.

4. Obtain the final weights and rankings of the engineering characteristics with respect to the goal. Compared to the ranking in the preceding HOQ, the AHP method results in rankings that are slightly different from those obtained using the PMM. The comparisons on the ranking of the engineering characteristics or technical descriptors (TD) are shown in Table 5.6.

In our illustrative example, the ranking of the engineering characteristics in the HOQ by the PMM is not the same as that by the AHP method. This might be due to differences between the procedures, and different comparisons given to the relative preferences.

Table 5.5   Pair-wise comparison of VOCs with respect to the goal.

	Cleanliness of physical facilities	The staff appearance	Cleanliness of restrooms	Variety of souvenirs	Availability of kiosks selling drinks, etc.	Interesting programs
Attractiveness of physical facilities	2.0	7.0	3.0	2.0	2.0	2.0
Cleanliness of physical facilities		5.0	2.0	1.0	1.0	1.0
The staff appearance			1/2	1/3	1/4	1/4
Cleanliness of restrooms				1.0	1/2	1/2
Variety of souvenirs					1.0	1.0
Availability of kiosks selling drinks, etc.						1.0

Table 5.6   Weights and ranking of the engineering characteristics.

	TD1	TD2	TD3	TD4	TD5	TD6	TD7	TD8	TD9
Importance in HOQ	424.6	389.4	481.0	315.3	301.1	329.7	164.6	196.1	350.3
Ranking in HOQ	2	3	1	6	7	5	9	8	4
Importance in AHP	0.132	0.108	0.141	0.085	0.088	0.090	0.075	0.086	0.195
Ranking in AHP	3	4	2	8	6	5	9	7	1

Comparison of the PMM and the AHP Method

AHP is a useful tool in decision making. QFD, as a product development tool that makes use of PMM, is promising as a decision-making technique and is being applied to a wide range of decision-making applications. Both techniques promise their users the means to organize related information, as well as a thorough evaluation of information, both quantitative and qualitative. In the following some comparative studies are discussed.

Number of Judgments Required

PMM generally requires fewer team judgments than does AHP. Using PMM, for *n* choices and two factors, the number of team judgments required is 2*n*. For *n* choices and three factors, the number of team judgments required is 3*n*. With AHP matrices, for *n* choices, the number of team judgments required is $n(n-1)/2$. The number of judgments needed for two and three factors by PMM and AHP are shown in Figure 5.2. From the figure, we can see that as the number of choices increases, the number of required judgments in the AHP method becomes very large.

Difficulty in Making Judgments

AHP judgments are often easier and quicker to make than PMM judgments. This is because AHP judgments are more intuitive, less focused on a single criterion, and less constrained than PMM judgments. Generally, comparisons between two alternatives are far more straightforward and simple than those for more than two alternatives, when considering one criterion at a time. In the AHP method, each pair-wise comparison is easier to make than an overall importance comparison, as is done in the PMM. For that very reason, AHP judgments are easier to understand than PMM judgments (Cohen, 1995).

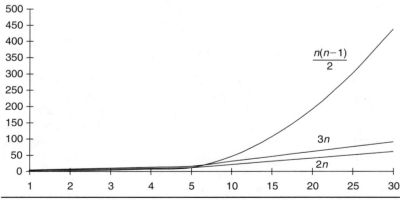

Figure 5.2   The number of judgments required: 2*n* for PMM with two factors, 3*n* for PMM with three factors, and $n(n-1)/2$ with AHP matrices.

Accuracy of the Judgments

Since the focus on the identification of VOCs is the driving force of QFD, considerable effort has to be committed to properly identifying those requirements. Sometimes a company may want a more precise and accurate analysis of the VOCs so that actions taken later can be more effective. In this case, the AHP method should be preferred. Through pair-wise comparisons, the AHP method can give the decision makers a better description of the WHATs. Whereas in the ordinary weight judgments in the HOQ, only the customers' rough judgments of the relative importance of the VOCs are given.

In practice, inconsistency in judgments cannot be totally avoided. It needs to be ensured, however, that the pair-wise comparisons do not contain too many inconsistencies. In AHP, we use the consistency ratio (CR) to measure the degree of inconsistency. If $CR \le 0.1$, the comparison is considered acceptable. If $CR > 0.1$, reassessment of the entries to reduce the inconsistency is required until the CR meets the practical standard. Thus, by using CR as an indicator, AHP can offer a better judgment of the factors in an HOQ.

Cost and Time Needed for Judgment

Although AHP can offer a more precise analysis of the VOCs, the cost of doing pair-wise comparisons is also higher. As explained previously, the number of team judgments required by AHP is $n(n-1)/2$, which is much more than the number of PMM judgments in a given HOQ. In industry, the lifecycle cost of a product must meet market expectations. To enter the market and be competitive with products from other producers, an industry must try to reduce cost, improve product marketability, and increase the return on investment. With regard to cost, the AHP method may have its shortcomings.

Overall, the AHP method can give an easier and more accurate analysis of VOCs in the HOQ, but it needs more time and financial resources. Compared with the AHP method, PMM requires less time because fewer judgments are needed.

As each of the two methods has its advantages and shortcomings, their proper use is essential. Some considerations for the choice of method are given here. Generally, the time and cost of improving the product are the major concerns of decision makers in industry. For a company to stay competitive and profitable, the price of a product has to be reduced as much as possible. Also, to capture a market in the presence of other competitors, time is very critical. When these two factors are of the uppermost concern,

PMM should be used to analyze VOCs, since it is straightforward, simple, and easy to use.

On the other hand, for a long-term outlook or competitive considerations, a company might want to carry out a much more precise analysis and identification of its VOCs. In that case, a more accurate resource allocation method, such as the AHP, is preferred. This is especially important for products and processes that are critical to the reputation of the company.

The two methods can also be done step-by-step so that a final relatively accurate analysis of VOCs can be achieved, especially when there are a large number and several levels of VOCs. PMM can be used at the factor screening stage. Screening is usually performed at the early stages of a project when it is likely that many factors that are initially considered have little or no effect on response. The factors that have been identified as important can then be investigated more thoroughly in subsequent stages. The decision maker can thus use the ordinary QFD method to first select the important VOCs. The AHP method can then be applied to rank these voices.

PMM and AHP each have their own merits. The AHP method can offer a more precise analysis, but requires more time and resources. PMM is easier to use, but the results might not be as accurate as what the AHP method can provide. With regard to which method is better for a particular industry or company, specific considerations based on the decision makers' needs are required.

INTEGRATION OF QFD AND DESIGN OF EXPERIMENTS

Use of DOE and QFD

Design of experiments (DOE) can be used to select the significant engineering characteristics to focus efforts on. They are usually performed by investigators through a series of tests in which changes are made systematically to the input variables of a process so that reasons for changes in the output responses can be identified. In recent years, experimental designs have become a widely accepted and frequently used approach for engineering product and process design, and for optimizing the production process.

To begin an experimental design, the factors to be investigated have to be selected first. Although the advantage of using statistically designed experimentation is to reduce the number of tests, the number of factors to be studied could be very large and have to be reduced to a manageable number. The experimenter may face the problem of deciding which factors are potentially significant and which would take precedence over the rest. Although the experimenter can use a fractional factorial experiment to screen out unimportant factors, the option may still be impracticable when there are a large number of factors.

At present, there is no systematic approach for factor selection in DOE. Usually, factor selection is governed more by the experimenter's experience, intuition, and gut feeling. Information relevant to the experiment is loosely scattered, undocumented, and unstructured. As a result, questions such as "Shouldn't we be testing factor A instead of factor B?" may arise halfway through a DOE project. The use of QFD can help answer this question, and a more systematic analysis can be presented with the help of QFD.

A Case Study

A prescribed method of factor selection is illustrated step by step through a case involving the use of a DOE study. The project aims to optimize one of the many processes found in printed circuit board manufacturing.

Background

The process under study is known within the industry as vacuum lamination. During this process, the different layers of a circuit board are pressed together using an autoclave vacuum press. Thickness variation arises in the circuit board because of imperfections in the setting of press parameters, such as temperature, pressure, and time. Other factors, such as type of material and viscosity of material at elevated temperature, could also affect the thickness.

The objective of the original project was to minimize the thickness variation of the boards, with a secondary objective of achieving an average thickness of 1.17mm. The product of interest is a four-layer printed circuit board known as a single in-line memory module (SIMM) that can commonly be found in personal computers. A special characteristic of a SIMM board is that it demands a very small thickness variation.

Many factors affect the thickness of a SIMM board. This case study looks at some of the important factors and studies their contribution to the variation in thickness of the SIMM board. The first step is to select the potentially important factors.

The Problem of Finding the Process Factors to be Tested in DOE

In the selection of the process factors to be tested in DOE, the problem of which factors should be chosen arises. Although some of the factors can be obtained through the experimenter's experience, a structured and complete set of factors is not easily found, for there are quite a large number of factors relating, in varying degrees, to different aspects of the problem.

On the other hand, testing all the factors in an experiment will cost too much in resources, effort, and time. This is even with the fractional factorial design, which can significantly reduce the number of experiment runs. In order to not drop any factor from the consideration directly, QFD is used here to select the most important few factors. DOE is then applied to these factors to better understand the process and to determine how the factors are related to the responses. The use of QFD can also assist the decision maker in selecting the factorial design setting.

Adapted HOQ Matrix of the Case

The present case study involves minimizing the thickness variation of printed circuit board manufacturing. A number of related technical objectives are identified. After discussion, an expanded list of all objectives pertaining to the problem is generated. They include:

1. Minimal thickness variation

2. Average thickness on target

3. Dimensional stability

4. No delamination

5. Minimal warpage

6. No voids

7. High copper peel strength

8. Fully cured prepregs

As with the technical objectives, a list of possible process factors was also generated and is as follows:

1. Material class

2. Pressure at Step 2 of press cycle

3. Temperature at Step 2 of press cycle

4. Curing temperature

5. Curing time

6. Low/normal flow prepregs

7. Curing pressure

8. Press pads

9. Rate of increase of temperature

10. Rate of decrease of temperature

11. Lay-up/construction

12. Prepreg to innercore thickness ratio

After all the technical objectives and the process factors are listed, the adapted HOQ matrix was built (see Figure 5.3).

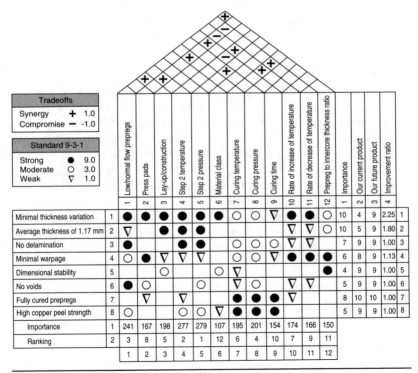

Figure 5.3 The HOQ used for selection of factors in DOE planning.

Result of the Case Study

We briefly discuss some possibilities, and then show the actual results. First if the number of factors to be used is fixed, then the absolute ranking can be used. For example, if three factors are to be selected, then factors 1, 4, and 5 should be used.

The HOQ can also be used to select the number of factors. If a small number of factors should be chosen, it is quite obvious that 1, 4, and 5 should be chosen, as their absolute weightages are all far over the next ranked. On the other hand, the importance of factors 3, 7, and 10 are quite close to each other, and they should be selected if up to six factors can be used.

In this case study, by considering the ranking and by taking into account the roof matrix in the adapted HOQ, a total of six factors were identified to be tested in the DOE. They are:

1. Fluidity of prepregs

2. Lay-up of the multi-layer boards

3. Use of press pads during the press cycle

4. Temperature at step 2 of the press cycle

5. Pressure at step 2 of press cycle

6. Material class of innercores

A fractional factorial experiment was then conducted to "screen out" the less significant factors from the more significant ones. The specific objective was to achieve a finished board thickness of 1.27mm with a variation of 6 percent for the SIMM board design as specified by the customer. The evaluation objective was to achieve the smallest possible variation after press thickness with the secondary objective of keeping the average after press thickness to around 1.17mm to allow for increase in thickness during the copper plating process.

The detail of the experiment and analysis is reported in Poh (1998). The analysis follows the standard design of experiment framework and will not be described here. Within the limits of the respective parameters set for this experiment, the following conclusions were drawn:

1. Lay-up causes the most significant thickness variation among the factors investigated.

2. Temperature should be set at the lower level.

3. Press pads should not be used.

4. A lower flow prepreg is preferred over a normal flow prepreg.

5. Material class of the innercore and pressure at step 2 of the press cycle does not significantly affect the thickness variation of the panels.

Although the variation cannot be considered complete, good results were obtained during the evaluation itself. The standard deviation of certain runs went as low as 0.017mm on average. This translates to a 99.74 percent confidence range of 0.102mm. Assuming a capable process, a range of 0.102mm will give a maximum thickness variation of 0.0501mm from the specified nominal thickness of 1.27mm. This gives roughly a 4 percent thickness variation. This 4 percent thickness variation gives ample allowance for additional variation due to the copper plating process.

The problem of identifying several relatively important factors to test in DOE when there are quite a large number of choices is an important one in experimental design. Here are technical, time, and other resource constraints. As an effective and widely used planning tool to connect "customer requirements" to "technical responses," and then to give the ranking of the "technical responses," QFD can be adapted and then applied to the factor selection part of DOE.

The effectiveness of adapted QFD in the factor selection process is very clear. There does not need to be any exclusion of possible factors. Other requirements or responses can also be taken into consideration. This provides a clear graphical representation of how the analysis and decision are made. When the number of factors has to be increased or reduced, the ranking and actual weightage provides an easy means for this adjustment. A case study has been used to illustrate the above.

Chapter 6
Benchmarking for Quality Improvement

In the previous chapters, the scope of the voice of the customer was extended into the future. Several methods were also proposed to capture customers' future voices. These were embedded into QFD analysis. In this way, practitioners can have a complete picture of customer requirements and also know what customers desire most. However, what we should know is beyond this scope, and more must be done than merely capturing the voice of the customer, especially in terms of competitive benchmarking. QFD practitioners must accurately and deeply understand the VOC so that they really know how they can achieve the desired customer satisfaction performance for each customer need.

To serve this purpose, two important questions need to be answered. The first is determination of desired level of customer satisfaction performance, that is, the issue of competitive analysis and target setting. Second, it is essential for QFD practitioners to have a clear idea about the nature of each customer need, that is, the issue of differentiation among customer requirements. This chapter focuses on customer satisfaction benchmarking, which is one of the approaches proposed for better understanding of the voice of the customer.

IMPORTANCE OF BENCHMARKING

As an integral part of the total quality process, *benchmarking is the search for industry best practices that lead to superior performance* (Camp, 1989). It is a productivity improvement tool that has received considerable attention among companies. Benchmarking helps to achieve and maintain competitive advantage by striving for world-class performance. By obtaining the information needed to support continuous improvement and gain competitive advantage, benchmarking can help QFD users make strategic decisions from both a marketing and a technical viewpoint: customer satisfaction benchmarking and technical benchmarking.

Customer satisfaction benchmarking can help decision makers identify areas for improvement, make strategic decisions, and set targets on ideal satisfaction performance level. Focusing on this aspect, this chapter discusses both the methodological and data analysis issues involved in this process. The use of hierarchical benchmarks in customer satisfaction benchmarking is also proposed. This is particularly useful for small- and medium-size enterprises (SMEs). For effective utilization, the benchmarking data are analyzed from the following three angles:

- Aggregate satisfaction

- Customer segments

- Data significance

The use of benchmarking in QFD provides opportunities to identify key areas for improvement. Vaziri (1992) suggested using competitive benchmarking to set goals and to achieve superior customer satisfaction. Swanson (1993) proposed a quality benchmark deployment technique, a variation of QFD, to help organizations logically select critical areas to benchmark and to understand the relationship between customer expectations and performance drivers. Lu et al. (1994) developed an integrative approach for strategic marketing by using QFD, AHP, and benchmarking.

Nevertheless, it may not be easy to select appropriate benchmarks and set goals based on the benchmarking information. Surveys also show that the analysis of benchmarking data is limited in the existing literature. Consequently, inappropriate decision making for targets and goals may result. For example, a decision could be based on sampling error rather than a real gap between customer perception of a company's and its competitor's products or services.

The two main purposes of this chapter are:

- To study and develop procedures that can be used in benchmark selection and information utilization for successful benchmarking in QFD

- To develop procedures and methods to analyze benchmarking data in a more detailed way for effective usage of data

The use of hierarchical benchmarks for strategic competitor selection and decision making may provide a road map to achieve world-class performance through benchmarking in QFD. This is especially true for SMEs or companies in developing countries. On the other hand, competitive data should be thoroughly analyzed in comparison with the data taken from the company's own process (Goetsch and Davis, 1997) for establishing gaps and setting goals. This chapter proposes several methods for investigating the benchmarking data, for example, use of cluster analysis and nonparametric tests.

It is recognized that there are four types of benchmarking: internal, competitive, functional, and generic (Camp, 1989).

- *Internal benchmarking* studies the best performers in an organization.

- *Competitive benchmarking* deals with the best competitors in an industry.

- *Functional benchmarking* investigates competitors or industry lead firms in similar functions.

- *Generic benchmarking* studies the best business practices in the world.

Some benefits of benchmarking include meeting customer requirements, establishing goals, measuring true productivity, becoming competitive, and ensuring that the best industry practices are included in work processes, generating broadly based change in organizational thinking and action. For some benchmarking literature surveys, see Jackson et al. (1994), Czuchry et al. (1995), and Zairi (1996).

Customer Satisfaction Benchmarking

To a large extent, the quality of a product or service is ultimately judged in terms of customer satisfaction. There are direct linkages between providing customer satisfaction and achieving a superior financial and competitive position. However, the cost of customer dissatisfaction could be very high. For example, recent work shows that 8.5 percent of revenue is at risk from customer dissatisfaction (Hepworth, 1997). Thus, for repeatable success, customer satisfaction is considered an important goal of an organization. Indeed, a group of satisfied customers is one of its key assets.

Customer satisfaction level is one of the critical success factors that are candidates for benchmarking (Camp, 1989). QFD can incorporate benchmarking information by extending the traditional QFD matrix. It utilizes benchmarking information primarily in the form of customer satisfaction benchmarking in the planning matrix and technical performance benchmarking in the technical matrix. A typical form of customer satisfaction benchmarking is shown in Figure 6.1.

Understanding customer perception is essential to remaining competitive nowadays. To do this, a company should know the degree of customer satisfaction not only with its current product or service, but also with that

		Importance	Customer satisfaction benchmarking				Improvement ratio	Final importance
			Our current product	Competitor 1	Competitor 2	Our future product		
Customer attribute	Good orientation program	5	2	4	3	4	2	10
	...		...	...	...	...	...	...

Figure 6.1   Customer satisfaction benchmarking in the planning matrix.

of its competitors. The degree of customer satisfaction reflects perception of how well customer wants and needs are being met. For example, consider the situation of new students arriving at a university. As far as the customer requirement "good orientation program" is concerned, students may perceive the current service as a 2 on a 1–5 scale (Figure 6.1). Similarly, customer satisfaction degree to competitors' products is the customer perception showing how well the products or services of competitors meet customers' wants and needs. Taking the same example, students may view competitors' services as 3 or 4 on a 1–5 scale, which suggests that customers are more satisfied with competitors' services when considering the feature "good orientation program." It is clear that comparison with competitors can identify opportunities for improvement.

Based on the customer satisfaction degree to both a company's and its competitors' products, a goal is to be determined to set the target for meeting each customer attribute. The goal combines the data describing customers' perception of the competitive position of the product or service relative to its competitors. The customer satisfaction degree is the customers' rating according to the current product, while the goal is the future-state rating to be reached. The goal is to put customer satisfaction benchmarking to work for the company in order to achieve world-class competitive capability. Setting the goal is a crucial and strategic step in QFD. Due to limited resources, trade-offs must be made in almost every case. It is reasonable to pay more attention to those more important customer attributes when setting goals. As Figure 6.1 shows, for requirement "good orientation program" the customer satisfaction level for the future service is set as 4. This is based on the consideration of the customer satisfaction benchmarking information and the degree of importance.

Just as with other benchmarking processes, customer satisfaction benchmarking is a continuous process of evaluating current performance, setting goals for the future, and identifying areas for improvement. The customer satisfaction benchmarking process in QFD is shown in Figure 6.2. The main components involved in this process are similar to those various benchmarking processes mentioned in the previous section. It is a rather straightforward process and can be naturally incorporated into traditional QFD. Particularly, it should be noted that customer satisfaction benchmarking in QFD is a never-ending process. Through this never-ending benchmarking process, continuous quality improvement can be achieved.

It is important to determine whether performance improvement really happens after implementing customer satisfaction benchmarking. The effectiveness of the benchmarking process in changing customer perceptions can be measured through customer satisfaction questionnaires. By comparing the difference between customer satisfaction levels before and after a benchmarking exercise is implemented, it is easy to identify whether a particular target has been achieved.

USE OF HIERARCHICAL BENCHMARKS

Benchmarking is a useful tool when products with the best-in-class features are used for comparison purposes. Best-in-class refers to the best product or service in a similar price classification and market segment. On the other hand, it is never easy to achieve world-class performance. Although in the

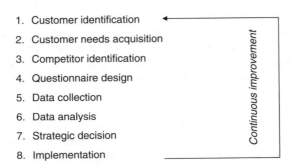

Figure 6.2   Customer satisfaction benchmarking process in QFD.

long run, to be world-class is the goal of many companies, it may be unrealistic for a product or service to achieve the same high level of performance by merely comparing against world-class companies, especially for most SMEs.

Hierarchical Benchmarks

The use of hierarchical benchmarks is described here. It may provide a step-by-step method to approach and/or realize the eventual goal of becoming best-in-class. Using this method, different benchmarks can be selected from various categories, each of which belongs to a different hierarchy. For example, benchmarks can be based on local-class, regional-class, or world-class categories. When measuring customer satisfaction, customers are usually more satisfied with products or services provided by world-class compared to local-class companies.

By using hierarchical benchmarks in customer satisfaction benchmarking, one company can easily locate its corresponding position in terms of customer satisfaction performance, for example, local-class, regional-class, or world-class products. Using hierarchical benchmarks can also help in identifying a company's strengths and weaknesses compared to competitors in each hierarchy. In other words, a company can have a clear idea of the customer satisfaction gap between its own and local-class, regional-class, or world-class. Furthermore, being able to reach one target class and set another higher class as its next goal can help the company gain confidence in knowing that it is moving toward world-class performance. Hence, this method should help companies identify key areas to improve.

Weightage Determination

Under different circumstances, a company will focus more on a certain benchmark in one hierarchy for customer satisfaction benchmarking. That is, the weights given to different hierarchical benchmarks will be different. For example, if customers perceive one company's product as being somewhere between local-class and regional-class, then it may be appropriate to consider regional-class as the most important benchmark. However, when it performs worse than local-class in terms of customer satisfaction, it may focus more on the local-class benchmark.

Some qualitative judgments on hierarchical benchmarks in terms of their relative importance are usually easy to reach, as illustrated above. However, quantitative measures of the weights assigned to different hierarchies should help QFD users acquire a better understanding and thereby lead to easier decision making.

Pair-wise comparison is a technique that can assist companies in acquiring the priority of each benchmarking hierarchy. Saaty's (1980) fundamental scale is recommended in that it has been widely used for making comparisons. That is, the 1–9 scale is employed to make distinctions, ranging from equally important to extremely important. Specifically, the value 9 should be used when a certain hierarchy is considered as extremely more important or appropriate than another one; while 1 would be used when two hierarchies have similar conditions.

The pair-wise comparison may help QFD users decide on which hierarchy they should benchmark. Nevertheless, it should be noted that when making pair-wise comparisons, it would be more appropriate to consider other factors that are also involved, rather than simply depending on the importance scores. One example would be on the availability of data.

Using Hierarchical Benchmarks

Suppose that the weight of each hierarchy is determined by following the above method. Let W_l, W_r, and W_w denote the weights given to local-class, regional-class, and world-class respectively; while S_{own}, S_l, S_r, and S_w represent the customer satisfaction levels of the product or service provided by the company itself, by a local-class organization, by a regional-class organization, and a world-class organization respectively (see Table 6.1).

Two methods are proposed to utilize benchmarking information based on hierarchical benchmarks, namely aggregate benchmark and principal benchmark. When using the aggregate benchmark method, all the information from different hierarchies will be considered. For target setting, decision makers should consider both customer satisfaction degrees to the

Table 6.1 Weights and customer satisfaction performance for hierarchical benchmarks.

	Local-class	Regional-class	World-class
Weightage	W_l	W_r	W_w
Customer satisfaction performance	S_l	S_r	S_w

company's product S_{own} and the overall customer satisfaction performance, which can be computed as

$$S_{agg} = S_l W_l + S_r W_r + S_w W_w$$

Under the principal benchmark method, decision makers usually only consider the competitor in a particular hierarchy that receives the highest weightage, that is, $S_{pri} = max \{S_l, S_r, S_w\}$. For example, if the company decides to focus on regional-class benchmarks, wherein W_r is much greater than W_l and W_w, only S_{own} and S_r should be obtained from a customer satisfaction survey. They will be taken into consideration when setting the future customer satisfaction performance.

Both the aggregate and principal benchmark methods have their own pros and cons. The aggregate benchmark can be adopted when sufficient resources are given, since customer satisfaction performance in each hierarchy will be evaluated. The first method should provide more useful information, but the second method requires less time and effort.

ANALYSIS OF BENCHMARKING DATA

In QFD, customer satisfaction benchmarking is usually carried out through the use of questionnaires, for example, the customer satisfaction questionnaire. Establishing the gaps and goal setting are based on data taken from the questionnaire. The benchmarking data should be carefully analyzed for strategic decision making. This section presents the necessity of and possible methods for performing data analysis from three perspectives: aggregate satisfaction degree, customer segments, and data significance.

Aggregate Satisfaction Degree

During benchmarking in QFD, the questionnaire usually yields information regarding customers' satisfaction level on an *individual requirement*. For each customer need, customers rate satisfaction level based on product performance in terms of this specific need. However, the availability of data on the degree of customers' *overall satisfaction* is often beneficial to decision makers. This is because the former reveals in which specific areas the product should be improved from a microperspective. The overall satisfaction may provide customers' perceptions as a whole, from a macroperspective. For example, when a customer decides to purchase something, his or her decision is usually based on an overall judgment rather than only dependent on a partial impression of the product. This phenomenon is easy to understand, since customers usually consider many related factors before making their final decision.

Based on the available data (the importance to customers and the satisfaction degree to individual statements), one solution could be to calculate the aggregate customer satisfaction degree. Denoted by I_i and S_i, the importance of and satisfaction degree to the ith customer requirement, the aggregate customer satisfaction S_{Ai} can be easily calculated by the following equation:

$$S_{Ai} = \frac{\sum_{i=1}^{m} I_i S_i}{\sum_{i=1}^{m} I_i} \tag{6.1}$$

where m is the number of customer requirements. S_{Ai} is normalized and thus has the same scale as S_i. That is, if S_i adopts a 1–5 scale, S_i also ranges from 1 to 5, which is easy for decision making. By applying the above method to customers' satisfaction rating of both a company's and a competitors' product, QFD users can capture customers' overall satisfaction and make use of it as benchmarking data.

Customer Segments

The needs of a substantial portion of the customers may be different from those of other customers. Consequently, segments probably exist among customers. Customers in different segments have different satisfaction levels, even for the same customer requirement. For example, for a certain customer need, it is possible that there are two different customer perceptions. Specifically, one segment of customers may perceive it as very satisfactory, while another segment of customers views it as very unsatisfactory.

It is useful to identify the existence of customer segments so that market share can be maximized. For example, when there are segments, three possible strategies could be:

- Develop different products for each segment

- Develop one product for a major segment

- Develop one product for a specific segment (not for a major segment, due mainly to the existence of strong competitors in that segment)

In conventional data analysis, a decision is made without consideration of customer segmentation. The data is utilized by simply taking the average value of different customer responses. However, the mean value may not represent the actual customer satisfaction level when there exist customer segments. For example, if we mix two extremes—very unsatisfactory and very satisfactory—the average customer satisfaction level would be neutral. As a result, the decision made based on this data may not appropriately serve the benchmarking purpose.

Another problem that results from customer segments is on the variability issue. Due to the nature of multiresponses for a questionnaire survey, the mean value of importance for each customer attribute has a corresponding variation. This variation could be transformed into the technical importance for each technical characteristic, which would affect the accuracy of technical ranking and resource allocation. It is clear that it is desirable to have less variation in the customer input data. Thus, if QFD users can successfully identify the possible customer segments and the target segments, the variation of each mean importance should decrease.

Before the customer satisfaction data is utilized, a checking for possible segments is necessary, and will provide much useful information. The data obtained from a customer satisfaction questionnaire can help QFD practitioners identify possible segments. Thus, from a certain point of view, customer satisfaction benchmarking provides a good means of detecting whether there are customer segments. In the cases where there probably exists customer segments, corresponding action should be taken. However, the existence of customer segments should be confirmed by further analysis and the target segments should also be identified.

A frequency histogram is one simple tool for identifying possible customer segments based on customer satisfaction benchmarking data. In such a histogram, a two dimensional graphical form is used. The horizontal axis represents the measurement scale, for example, a 5-point scale ranging from 1 to 5, while the vertical axis represents the frequency scale (the number of responses). It probably suggests that there is no customer segment when it is found that only one frequency scale stands out. However, it may indicate that there are possible customer segments when there are two or more similar frequency scales standing out. For instance, suppose two major groups of respondents were identified. One group perceives a particular attribute as being "very satisfactory," while the other considers it as "not so satisfactory." This information suggests that QFD users should take a deeper look at the differences between these two groups of customers.

Another approach to segmenting customers is cluster analysis, a technique for grouping individuals or objects into clusters. Objects in the same cluster are more like each other than they are like objects in other clusters.

The resulting object clusters should then exhibit high internal (within-cluster) homogeneity and high external (between-cluster) heterogeneity (Hair et al., 1998). Cluster analysis usually involves partitioning, interpretation, validation, and profiling. Punj and Stewart (1983) provided a comprehensive review of the application of the clustering methodology to marketing problems. They also use both theoretical and empirical findings to suggest which clustering options may be most useful to a particular research problem.

The frequency histogram method is straightforward and easy to visualize. However, it should be noted that the frequency histogram is performed on each set of data for each customer attribute. Interpreting the results from many histograms would be tedious, and sometimes it may be unrealistic when the results from different customer attributes are inconsistent with each other. Therefore, the frequency histogram may not be considered as a formal technique for segment identification and confirmation. Instead, it may be more suitable for performing preliminary analysis.

On the other hand, cluster analysis may provide a systematic approach to investigating possible customer segments. With the help of many statistical packages, it is easy to perform cluster analysis, even without knowing the underlying basis. However, since its application is more an art than a science, it can easily be abused (misapplied) by the analyst (Hair et al., 1998). Therefore, considerable attention should be given to the analysis and interpretation of results when adopting the cluster analysis method.

Significance of Benchmarking Data

The benchmarking data should be analyzed in terms of statistical significance. As mentioned, during the customer satisfaction benchmarking process, a common way to obtain the customer perception of each product is to average the respondents' input. Based on the different mean values of customers' perceptions on one's own and one's competitors' products, QFD practitioners can set the goal for the future. Other related information may also be taken into account, such as the importance level. However, the difference can be due to sampling error. This error arises because the observed mean is only an estimate of the population mean. It has an inherent error, since it is based only on a sample of data. Therefore, it is necessary to know whether the degree of difference between the data sets is due to factors other than sampling error.

It should be noted that knowing clearly whether the difference is significant enough is essential to a successful benchmarking effort. For example, based on a relatively higher mean value of customer satisfaction, one may conclude that they are performing better than one's competitors. However, it may not be the case when the difference in customer satisfaction is not statistically significant. Obviously, without testing the level of significance, inaccurate information may result in inaccurate decisions.

In view of the above, the use of statistics is proposed to incorporate data reliability analysis into customer satisfaction benchmarking. Specifically, nonparametric tests can be used to test the level of the significance of the difference identified through benchmarking. The advantage of performing this test is that the data need not be quantitative, but can be categorical or rank data. If there is only one competitor, the Wilcoxon rank sum test may be used to test the null hypothesis that the probability distributions associated with two populations are equivalent against the alternative hypothesis that one population probability distribution is shifted to the right (or left) of the other. When there are two or more competitors, the Kruskal-Wallis H test may be adopted. For more information on performing these tests, refer to, among others, Mendenhall and Sincich (1995). These tests are available in most statistics software packages.

After performing the test of significance, if it is found that there is no statistically significant difference between customer perceptions on a company's own product or service and the competitors', there are at least two possibilities to which benchmarking facilitators should pay attention. The first scenario could be that there is actually no significant difference at all. That is, customers view that each of the products (the company's own or the competitors') can give almost the same level of satisfaction with regard to a certain customer need.

Second, it may be the case that customers' perceptions of each product are different, but the results of the questionnaire may not reveal the difference. This possibility could be caused by the survey or by the customer satisfaction questionnaire. In this case, benchmarking facilitators may have to recheck the questionnaire and redo the survey. If there are no apparent reasons that could cause the nonsignificance, it may be concluded that the actual customer perceptions are very similar.

Benchmarking data can also be used in discriminate analysis. By using the discriminant loadings, one can accomplish the following:

1. Determine whether statistically significant differences exist between the average score profiles of the two defined groups *a priori.*

2. Establish procedures for classifying statistical units (individuals or objects) into groups on the basis of their scores on several variables.

3. Determine which of the independent variables account for most of the differences in the average score profiles of the two groups (Hair et al., 1998).

DISCUSSION

By benchmarking customer satisfaction, QFD users can understand how customers perceive their products or services versus their competitors', and they may further identify areas for quality improvement and competitive advantage. For successful customer satisfaction benchmarking in QFD, this chapter discussed the benchmarking process and suggested the use of the hierarchical benchmark method. The weightage determination for each hierarchical benchmark was discussed. Two specific methods of utilizing benchmarking information—aggregate benchmark and principal benchmark—were proposed. It is hoped that the use of hierarchical benchmarks would provide a road map to world-class performance through benchmarking, especially for SMEs and companies in developing countries.

This chapter further discussed the importance of data analysis from three aspects: aggregate satisfaction, customer segment, and level of data significance. Various techniques were suggested for performing the data analysis to its best usage. Frequency histogram and cluster analysis could help identify potential customer segments. Nonparametric tests could be used to test the significance of benchmarking data. Comparisons between these methods were also presented. Such data analyses may help avoid common pitfalls during benchmarking and thereby provide a basis for successful benchmarking in QFD.

Chapter 7

Integrating Kano's Model into QFD

The planning matrix of QFD helps product developers during strategic planning in such a way that they can decide on aspects of the planned product to be emphasized during the development process. The raw priorities based on customer input reflect what customers want most. However, the real information needed in QFD is which customers a company wants to satisfy most (Zultner, 1990) and how to meet those requirements.

Previous chapters extended the voice of the customer into the future and suggested a number of techniques for ensuring the successful implementation of customer satisfaction benchmarking in QFD. Although they have different approaches, they have very similar targets: to reprioritize customer requirements in order to achieve total customer satisfaction, the ultimate goal of QFD. It can be found that all customer attributes are treated as similar items except that their weights may be different. However, as Cohen (1995) argued, not only are some needs more important to the customer than others, but some are also important to the customer in different ways than others. The nature of each customer need and, therefore, the value that can be delivered to customers, may vary.

The Kano model provides an effective approach to categorizing customer attributes and helps understand the nature of these requirements (Kano et al., 1984; Matzler and Hinterhuber, 1998). It should give QFD users a new way of knowing customer requirements. For better implementation of QFD by differentiating customer requirements, there is a need to develop methods for integrating QFD and Kano's model. The newly developed approach described in this chapter may provide QFD users a means of achieving total customer satisfaction in an economical way.

PRIORITIZATION FOR CUSTOMER SATISFACTION

As mentioned, a typical planning matrix includes information on raw importance, competitive analysis, targets, improvement ratio, sales point, and final importance. Competitive analysis is one common method for adjusting the raw importance in the traditional planning matrix. By comparing one's product or service performance in meeting customers' needs with the key competition's performance, QFD users can benchmark their customer satisfaction and strategically set the target. Consequently, multiplied by the improvement ratio, the raw importance can be adjusted. Here we focus on the adjustment of raw importance based on the improvement ratio.

In the traditional importance adjustment technique, the relationship between customer satisfaction improvement ratio and importance increment ratio is treated as linear. In other words, it is assumed that a certain percentage of customer satisfaction improvement can be achieved by increasing the same percentage on the product or service performance. This, however, may not be true under actual circumstances.

It is correct that paying more attention to a customer attribute can lead to its better performance, and thereby higher customer satisfaction can be achieved. However, the relationship may not be simply linear. For some customer attributes, customer satisfaction can be greatly increased with only a small improvement in performance; while for some other features, customer satisfaction will only marginally increase even when the performance of the product has been greatly improved. For example, customers may take "no scratches" for granted when they purchase a new car. Therefore, there may not be a high satisfaction level even though this attribute is greatly improved. But, one tiny scratch on the hood of the car may put off a potential customer. As a converse example, an integrated child seat may delight potential customers.

Even for the same customer attribute, it is possible that the improvement ratio of customer satisfaction differs when improving its performance. For example, as the importance value increases and the performance improves, it will be more difficult to improve the customer satisfaction further. In other words, the marginal utility of performance improvement observes a decreasing function.

For the importance adjustment method, the relationship between the customer satisfaction improvement ratio and the importance increment is more complicated than linear. Using the traditional way of adjusting the raw importance, possibly the customer will not be satisfied with a certain customer attribute, or perhaps the customer satisfaction target will be overfulfilled.

Both of these two cases may not result in total customer satisfaction, or may achieve it in an effective way.

UNDERSTANDING CUSTOMER SATISFACTION WITH KANO'S MODEL

Quality can be defined as "satisfying or exceeding customer requirements and expectations." Thus, it is the customer who ultimately judges quality. Sometimes customer dissatisfaction can result in a huge loss to the company. Many customers seldom complain when a product's quality does not meet their expectations, and simply switch to a competitor's or to an alternative product to fulfill their needs for their next purchase.

The Kano Model

To maintain customer satisfaction and thereby long-run profitability, it is clear that companies should provide products of high quality. It is easy to understand that higher product performance can result in higher customer satisfaction. In a systematic way, Professor Kano (1984) and other researchers have developed a very useful diagram for characterizing customer needs (see Figure 7.1).

The Kano model can help us gain a profound understanding of customer satisfaction. It divides product features into the following three distinct categories, each of which affects customer satisfaction in a different way:

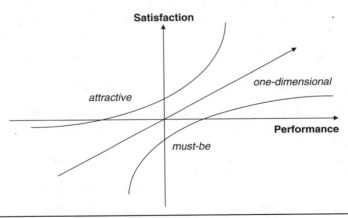

Figure 7.1   The Kano model (adapted from Kano, 1984).

- *Must-be attributes.* Customers take them for granted when fulfilled. For example, when a customer wants to buy a new car, "no scratches" may be such an attribute. However, if the product does not meet this basic need sufficiently, the customer may become very dissatisfied.

- *One-dimensional attributes.* These attributes result in customer satisfaction when fulfilled and dissatisfaction when not fulfilled. The better the attributes are, the better the customer likes them, for example, "low fuel consumption." These attributes are also known as *spoken qualities* of the product or service.

- *Attractive attributes.* The absence of attractive attributes does not cause dissatisfaction, because they are not expected by customers, who may be unaware of such product features. However, strong achievement in these attributes delights customers. Examples of such attributes are "power rearview mirror" and "remote door lock on ignition key."

The Kano model illustrates the relationship between customer satisfaction and the performance of products or services. This relationship differs depending on whether it is gauged according to attractive, one-dimensional, or must-be attributes. Kano's model provides an effective approach to categorizing customer attributes into different types. A competitive strategy for developing products and services should take into account these three categories. For examples of recent discussions on Kano's model, see Matzler and Hinterhuber (1998) and Shen et al. (2000).

It should be noted that the same attribute may change its category over time. Specifically, attractive attributes can become one-dimensional attributes, and then further become must-be attributes. We may perceive "power rearview mirror" as an attractive attribute this year, but it may be considered one-dimensional next year. Similarly, power door locks have now become a must-be attribute. Inherent in Kano's thinking is that customer needs (and consequently, product attributes) are dynamic rather than static.

Some Direct Implications on Product Development

Based on the Kano model, it can be recognized that customer satisfaction is more than a one-level issue as traditionally viewed. It may not be enough to merely satisfy customers by meeting their basic and spoken requirements in today's highly competitive environments. One main reason is that nowadays there are many similar products for customers to choose from in the marketplace. Customers might become confused when faced with many kinds of products in various brands and models, and their attention may not be attracted by ordinary or nonoutstanding products.

A strategy that many companies may adopt is to delight customers and to exceed their expectations. Through the offer of products with attractive quality, customers may be retained and thereby market share can be captured and sustained. Essentially, customer requirements and expectations can be satisfied and exceeded with such products. Furthermore, a satisfied customer is an effective medium for advertising a product that brings him or her exceeded satisfaction. The customer may share this satisfaction with other potential customers: friends, colleagues, and relatives, for example. It is therefore necessary to innovate, as Deming (1993) stated, to predict the needs of customers and give them more, because a satisfied customer may switch.

Hence, much attention should be paid to attractive quality creation when managing product development. Most innovative products cannot be designed and manufactured accidentally. A systematic approach is necessary for developing such products. In fact, one task of product management is to find out what makes a product superior, of higher value, or distinctive, and to deliver this to the customer better than the competition can. If such customer needs can be identified and designed into new products and marketing programs, the company will more likely succeed (Urban and Hauser, 1993).

Another important consideration we can learn from Kano's model is the timely delivery of innovative products. According to the model, attractive attributes become one-dimensional attributes over time, and then become basic attributes. In other words, those products that were perceived as innovative some time ago are no longer considered as innovative at the present time. Consequently, customer satisfaction may not be achieved and exceeded. Timely development and introduction of products with innovative features are, thus, important.

Existing Research

In the QFD literature, the Kano model can be applied to the process in the form of assigning weights to the customer attributes. Islam and Liu (1995) grouped customer needs into three subgroups: basic, one-dimensional, and excitement features. For each requirement, the raw importance is adjusted by multiplying a weight that is calculated using the AHP method. Similarly, using the Dual Importance Grid, Robertshaw (1995) classified types of Kano elements and suggested that customer needs should be reprioritized. The first priority is to deliver what is expected. The next is to deliver what is specified. The last is to provide the attractive elements.

However, the selection of weights is very subjective. It can also be seen that the relationship between customer satisfaction and customer attribute performance is still treated as linear, even after different weights are assigned to the corresponding Kano categories as shown above. The only difference in doing this is that the slopes are not the same. They could be larger or smaller than "1" according to the different Kano categories.

Matzler and Hinterhuber (1998) proposed a methodology, based on Kano's model of customer satisfaction, to explore customers' stated needs and unstated desires, and to segment them into different categories that have different impacts on customer satisfaction. However, it may be noticed that these two techniques were simply combined, and there is no systematic way of integrating them. Specifically, the Kano model was used to analyze different customer attributes in the QFD process. It did not address how to further utilize the information obtained from the Kano analysis, which should be at least as important as the Kano analysis itself.

Adjustment of Improvement Ratio

The relationship between customer satisfaction and product or service performance existing in the Kano model can be approximately quantified by using an appropriate function with parameters. Specifically, the relationship can be expressed as $s = f(k,p)$, where s represents the customer satisfaction; p represents the product or service performance; and k is the adjustment parameter for each Kano category.

It is obvious that better performance will lead to better customer satisfaction. However, Kano's model tells us more than this. It teaches us that not all customer satisfaction attributes are equal. As Figure 7.1 shows, attractive attributes are more likely to result in customer satisfaction than must-be attributes are. Moreover, for attractive attributes, customer satisfaction increases progressively with improvement in product performance. Therefore, for attractive attributes, we have

$$\frac{\Delta s}{s} > \frac{\Delta p}{p}$$

where s and p respectively represent the customer satisfaction degree and product performance level; Δs and Δp, respectively, represent the small shifts of s and p. Similarly, for one-dimensional attributes, $\Delta s/s = \Delta p/p$; and for must-be attributes, $\Delta s/s < \Delta p/p$.

To put it simply, the relationship between $\Delta s/s$ and $\Delta p/p$ is assumed to be linear. Consequently, by introducing a parameter k, the above three relationships can be expressed by a single equation, $\Delta s/s = k \cdot \Delta p/p$. For attractive attributes, $k > 1$; for one-dimensional attributes, $k = 1$; for must-be attributes, $0 < k < 1$.

The following relationship can be further obtained:

$$s = cp^k \tag{7.1}$$

where c is a constant. Also, let s_0 be the current customer satisfaction degree and p_0 be the performance level of the product or service. Furthermore let s_1 and p_1 be the customer satisfaction target and the desired performance. We assume that Equation (7.1) does not change with the change of status. That is, for both current and target status, Equation (7.1) is tenable. Thus, it can be seen that $s_0 = cp_0^k$ and $s_1 = cp_1^k$. Consequently, the following relationship can be obtained:

$$\frac{s_1}{s_0} = \frac{cp_1^k}{cp_0^k} = \left(\frac{p_1}{p_0}\right)^k \tag{7.2}$$

It should be noted that s_1/s_2 is the traditional improvement ratio denoted as IR_0. Therefore, we get the following approximate transformation function for the *adjusted improvement ratio:*

$$IR_{adj} = \left(IR_0\right)^{\frac{1}{k}} \tag{7.3}$$

Here IR_{adj} is the adjusted improvement ratio; IR_0 is the original improvement ratio; k is the Kano parameter varying from different categories.

In Equation (7.3), k is the only parameter for QFD practitioners to choose. After classifying customer attributes into appropriate Kano categories, the corresponding k can be chosen. For example, a possible set of k values could be "1/2," "1," and "2" for must-be, one-dimensional, and attractive attributes respectively. Consequently, the improvement ratio can be adjusted using Equation (7.3).

AN INTEGRATION PROCESS MODEL

To achieve total customer satisfaction in an effective way, QFD practitioners should not only know what customers want most, but also understand how much attention should be paid to each customer need in order to achieve the desired customer satisfaction level. The final adjusted importance may provide exactly this useful information. Figure 7.2 proposes a detailed process model based on the above discussions. It integrates Kano's model into QFD to adjust the raw importance of the customer attributes.

As Figure 7.2 shows, the first step in this process is to gather the customer requirements. Interviewing customers and gathering customer complaints are two of the most commonly used methods to find out what customers want. Usually, by using a questionnaire survey, customers are asked to prioritize their requirements. The competitive analysis is also conducted by asking them to rate their satisfaction degree for each customer attribute, for both one's own product or service and the competitors'. Consequently, customer attributes' raw priorities and customers' perceptions are collected. After setting the customer satisfaction target, the improvement ratio can be calculated as:

Improvement ratio (IR) = (Target) / (Our current customer satisfaction level)

With the help of QFD facilitators, for example, the provision of a brief introduction to the Kano model, customers are further asked to group their requirements into the proper categories. After grouping customer attributes into their proper Kano categories and choosing the appropriate transformation function as discussed earlier, the adjusted improvement ratio can be calculated by applying the transformation function to the traditional improvement ratio. The key difference between the original improvement ratio and the adjusted ratio is that the former represents the desired increment of the customer satisfaction degree, while the latter represents what we should do

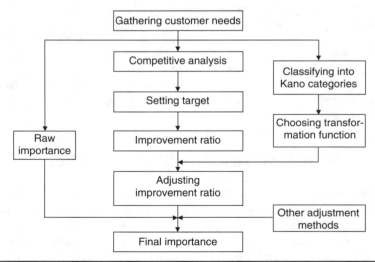

Figure 7.2 Quantitative VOC adjustment process based on the Kano model.

so as to achieve the desired customer satisfaction degree. For QFD practitioners, what they really want to know is the latter, the adjusted improvement ratio.

Finally, multiplied by the adjusted improvement ratio, the raw importance for each customer attribute can be adjusted into the final importance. Note that other methods using different adjustment factors, such as the trend of importance, may also be incorporated into the calculation of the final adjusted importance.

In this proposed approach, there are mainly two issues with which QFD practitioners must confront: classifying customer attributes into Kano categories, and choosing a proper transformation function for the customer attributes in each Kano category. The latter issue has been discussed in the previous section. The classification process is the main topic of the following discussion. Each identified customer requirement will be analyzed on the basis of Kano's model at this stage. The team can group these requirements into their appropriate Kano categories using the standard Kano questionnaire or the proposed force-choice classification method.

The Kano Questionnaire

In 1984, Professor Kano developed a methodology for identifying which customer attributes are must-be, which are one-dimensional, and which are attractive. The data needed in classifying customer attributes are obtained through a Kano questionnaire that consists of a pair of questions (one positive and one negative). For more information on the design and analysis of the Kano questionnaire, see Kano et al. (1984). King (1995) argued that unsolicited complaints are most often must-be quality; one-dimensional attributes are most often identified by surveys; and attractive items are those that suppliers develop, based on new insights and breakthroughs.

For instance, suppose that the product to be developed is a Web page. One of the identified customer requirements might be "the Web page is fast in loading." The pair of questions would be: (i) how would you feel if the Web page is fast in loading and (ii) how would you feel if the Web page is not fast in loading? For both questions, customers choose from one of the following responses: "delighted," "expect and like it," "no feeling," "live with it," "do not like it," or "other." Based on the Kano survey results, customer attributes can be categorized as "must-be," "one-dimensional," "attractive," "indifferent," "reverse," or "skeptical." For more information on the design and analysis of the questionnaire, see Kano et al. (1984).

A Force-choice Classification Method

The Kano questionnaire provides a systematic way of grouping customer requirements into different Kano categories. This grouping can be further improved by using a two-step classification method to distinguish categories to a deeper degree. Specifically, subcategories can be formed from the various Kano categories. For instance, "interesting Web page" may be categorized by customers as an attractive element. Among all attractive elements, however, it may be of interest to further understand how attractive it would be: extremely attractive or somewhat attractive.

In the first step, customers are asked to group their attributes into three basic Kano categories: must-be, one-dimensional, and attractive. Note that they must become familiar with the Kano model before the survey is conducted. Therefore, before the first step, the development team members or marketing people should provide respondents with a brief introduction to the Kano model.

For the second step, customers are asked to further group customer attributes into subcategories using the force-choice scale (see Figure 7.3). For those customer attributes grouped into the attractive category in the first step, customers further group them into one of three corresponding subcategories:, very attractive, moderately attractive, or somewhat attractive. Similarly, for those customer attributes grouped into the must-be category in the first step, customers further group them into one of three corresponding subcategories, that is, very basic, moderately basic, or somewhat basic. The customer attributes grouped as one-dimensional in the first step still remain in the same category because of its relative simplicity.

It should be noted that this method presumes that each customer attribute will fall into one of the three basic Kano categories. However, at

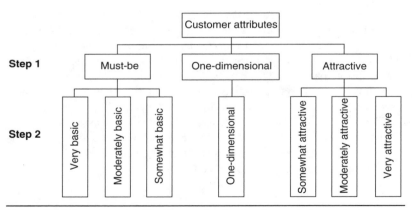

Figure 7.3 Two-step classification method using force-choice scale.

times, customers may not be able to express their opinion of whether a particular product or a particular feature of a product fulfills their needs. In this case, it may be classified as indifferent rather than in one of the three main categories.

DISCUSSION

Classifying customer requirements into their appropriate Kano categories and subcategories helps us understand different requirements for future products. Some product attributes can only make sure that customers will not be dissatisfied, while others can delight customers. The general guideline would be to seek to fulfill all must-be requirements, be competitive with market leaders on the one-dimensional attributes, and include some differentiating attractive elements (CQM, 1993). However, if QFD users follow the suggested improvement ratio adjustment method, the transformation function in Equation (7.3) for each customer attribute will be chosen, and its improvement ratio can be adjusted accordingly.

Furthermore, the completeness of customer requirements should be checked according to the results. That is, we should ensure that we have a comprehensive list of customer attributes in terms of different Kano categories. It is very useful for the identification of must-be and attractive attributes because they are considered as unspoken qualities. For instance, if there are very few customer requirements that are grouped as attractive attributes, corresponding action should be taken. More of this type of attributes should be gathered and embedded into future products in order to delight customers. This can be accomplished through in-depth interviews or by using the lead user analysis method (von Hippel, 1986). Alternatively, the project team may return to the previous stage and redefine customers or even go back further to reexamine the initial product idea.

Several issues involved in the Kano approach need to be further discussed. The first one is regarding the results of the Kano questionnaire analysis. Customer attributes can be categorized into three basic Kano categories: must-be, one-dimensional, and attractive. In addition to these three outcomes, other possible results could be indifferent, reverse, and skeptical (Kano et al., 1984). However, the proposed approach is mainly concerned with adjusting the improvement ratio for the three basic Kano categories. In other words, the proposed transformation function is not applicable to other possible categories. In this case, a possible way is to overlook the indifferent customer attributes because customers have no feeling of satisfaction or dissatisfaction regardless of whether or not their needs have been fulfilled. Regarding other outcomes, the questionnaire and its analysis may be modified (CQM, 1993).

Another point is on the selection of the value for parameter k. Equation (7.1) is a simple function to approximately quantify what the Kano model represents and tells us. In this simplified function, k is an important parameter that can be used to reflect different Kano categories. How to choose an appropriate numerical value for k is a critical issue. The selection of a k value is basically dependent on QFD practitioners' experience and understanding of relationships. Nevertheless, it should be noted that QFD practitioners might choose different numerical values for k as long as they think the chosen values can appropriately reflect the real relationship.

In addition, the basic categories may be further classified into subcategories in order to achieve a better understanding of the information that Kano's model provides. For example, attractive attributes may be further classified into one of the "some attractive," "moderately attractive," and "very attractive" subcategories. The use of subcategories may differentiate customer requirements more deeply and therefore provide more useful information. Consequently, the numerical value for parameter k would be slightly different for different subcategories although they follow the same trend: either convex or concave.

AN ILLUSTRATIVE EXAMPLE

In this section, an example is presented to show how the Kano model can be integrated into QFD by adjusting the raw priority of each customer attribute. QFD was applied to an example for the definition and design of "a good Web page" (Tan et al., 1998).

After careful information gathering, several main customer attributes and their corresponding priorities (using a 1–5 scale) were identified. Also, two Web pages were chosen to make a competitive analysis, *Competitor 1* and *Competitor 2*. Customers were asked to rate their satisfaction degree for both the company's own Web page and two competitors' based on the 1–5 scale. The data are presented in Table 7.1.

To implement this integrative approach, customers were asked to properly group their requirements into the Kano categories. The results of the Kano questionnaire are also given in Table 7.1. In this particular example, other raw importance adjustment methods (among them, sales point) were not taken into account, with the aim to illustrate this proposed process in a clear way.

Let us look at the traditional process first. As mentioned, the customer perception data are usually used to perform a benchmarking analysis. Based

Table 7.1 The VOC with customer perception and Kano categories.

Customer attribute	Raw importance	Customer perception			Kano category
		Our Web page	Competitor 1	Competitor 2	
Interesting Web pages	4	2	2	3	O
Easy-to-read text	3	2	3	3	M
Uniform and standardized	2	4	3	4	O
Sufficient information	3	3	4	3	M
Easy-to-locate information	3	4	3	5	O
Good linkages	5	2	3	4	A
Good integration of links	4	3	2	4	M
Fast in loading	5	3	4	2	O

O = one-dimensional A = attractive M = must-be

on the competitive analysis, a customer satisfaction target is set for each customer attribute. Through the adjustment of the improvement ratio, the raw importance can be consequently adjusted (see Figure 7.4).

The adjusted importance may not accurately represent what we really need. Take the customer attribute "easy-to-read text" as an example. For this customer attribute, the customer satisfaction target is set as "3." Thus, the customer satisfaction degree has to be increased by 150 percent in order to achieve the satisfaction target and to satisfy customers. To achieve this target, the raw importance was increased by 150 percent accordingly in the traditional planning matrix.

According to the previous Kano model analysis, this was judged as a must-be attribute. As a must-be attribute, the Kano model clearly tells us that the customer satisfaction target cannot be achieved even after increasing the raw importance by 150 percent. In fact, for this must-be attribute, more than 150 percent should be increased to achieve its desired customer satisfaction.

Following the newly developed approach, the Kano model was integrated into the planning matrix in order to achieve a deep and accurate understanding of the VOC. This was accomplished by adjusting the improvement ratio. According to Equation (7.2) and the proposed k value (see Figure 7.5), the improvement ratio can be changed into the adjusted improvement ratio. For customer requirement "easy-to-read text," the adjusted improvement ratio was 2.25 (= 1.5^2). Furthermore, multiplied by the adjusted improvement ratio, the raw importance of each customer attribute was adjusted with the incorporation of the Kano analysis (see Figure 7.5).

	Raw importance	Competitive analysis	Our Web page	Competitor 1	Competitor 2	Min = 2.0 ☆ Our Web page △ Competitor 1 ▽ Competitor 2 Max = 5.0	Target	Improvement ratio	Adjusted importance	Percent importance	Max = 30.0 Percent importance Min = 0.0
Interesting Web pages	4.0	✕	2.0	2.0	3.0		3.0	1.50	6.00	14.5	
Easy-to-read text	3.0	✕	2.0	3.0	3.0		3.0	1.50	4.50	10.8	
Uniform and standardized page design	2.0	✕	4.0	3.0	4.0		4.0	1.00	2.00	4.8	
Sufficient information	3.0	✕	3.0	4.0	3.0		4.0	1.33	4.00	9.6	
Easy-to-locate information	3.0	✕	4.0	3.0	5.0		4.0	1.00	3.00	7.2	
Good linkages	5.0	✕	2.0	3.0	4.0		4.0	2.00	10.00	24.1	
Good integration of links	4.0	✕	3.0	2.0	4.0		4.0	1.33	5.33	12.9	
Fast in loading	5.0	✕	3.0	4.0	2.0		4.0	1.33	6.67	16.1	

Figure 7.4   The traditional planning matrix for "a good Web page."

Kano Category	
Attractive	A	2.0
One-dimension	O	1.0
Must-be	M	0.5

	Raw importance	Kano category	Competitive analysis	Our Web page	Competitor 1	Competitor 2	Min = 2.0 ☆ Our Web page △ Competitor 1 ▽ Competitor 2 Max = 5.0	Target	Improvement ratio	Adjusted importance ratio	Adjusted importance	Adjusted importance	Max = 30.0 Percent importance Min = 0.0
Interesting Web pages	4.0	O	✕	2.0	2.0	3.0		3.0	1.50	1.50	6.00	13.7	
Easy-to-read text	3.0	M	✕	2.0	3.0	3.0		3.0	1.50	2.25	6.75	15.4	
Uniform and standardized page design	2.0	O	✕	4.0	3.0	4.0		4.0	1.00	1.00	2.00	4.6	
Sufficient information	3.0	M	✕	3.0	4.0	3.0		4.0	1.33	1.77	5.31	12.1	
Easy-to-locate information	3.0	O	✕	4.0	3.0	5.0		4.0	1.00	1.00	3.00	6.8	
Good linkages	5.0	A	✕	2.0	3.0	4.0		4.0	2.00	1.41	7.05	16.1	
Good integration of links	4.0	M	✕	3.0	2.0	4.0		4.0	1.33	1.77	7.08	16.1	
Fast in loading	5.0	O	✕	3.0	4.0	2.0		4.0	1.33	1.33	6.65	15.2	

Figure 7.5   The planning matrix with Kano category.

The planning matrix with Kano categories in Figure 7.5 shows that the raw priorities are adjusted differently from that using the traditional method. The final priority of customer requirements has, therefore, been changed. Take the customer attribute "easy-to-read text" as an example again. In the traditional planning matrix, its percentage importance is 10.8 percent This becomes 15.4 percent after incorporating the Kano analysis. Thus, the importance has been increased just as what we previously analyzed. For other customer attributes, the outcomes are also similar. Although it may not be demonstrated that this adjusted importance for the customer attribute "easy-to-read text" is the most appropriate, the conclusion may be reached that it does provide QFD practitioners (Web page designers) with a better and more reasonable importance value.

Another finding from this example is that only one customer attribute ("good linkages") belongs to the attractive Kano category in this particular case. It is known that attractive attributes can lead to exciters and delighters and expand customer expectations (Langley et al., 1996). Therefore, it is necessary for the Web page designers to collect other attractive customer attributes, for example, via lead user analysis (von Hippel, 1986) or in-depth interviews, and incorporate them into the VOC such that comprehensive customer attributes in all three Kano categories can be included.

As the ultimate goal of QFD, customer satisfaction should be achieved totally and effectively. The Kano model can be used to help differentiate between customer requirements and to obtain an imaginative understanding of customer needs (Eureka and Ryan, 1994). In this chapter, a customer satisfaction-related problem in the traditional QFD process was raised. Based on the Kano model, the concept of customer satisfaction was analyzed and it was suggested to exceed customer satisfaction using attractive quality elements. Further, the existing problem was solved using a proposed improvement ratio adjustment function, which is based, partly, on the Kano model.

In order to implement the proposed adjustment method, an integrative process model based on the Kano model and QFD was proposed to help QFD practitioners understand the nature of the VOC. An example was used to illustrate the proposed procedure for adjusting the traditional improvement ratio. This example also showed that the proposed approach helps to check the completeness of the VOC.

Chapter 8
QFD for Service Quality Analysis

Q FD has traditionally been used in product design. The use of QFD in process design is straightforward. However, because the objective in product and process design is to serve the customer, one should consider issues associated also with service quality. Delivering high service quality is a successful strategy for increasing an organization's performance in order to thrive in the intense competition both domestically and internationally (Rao and Kelkar, 1997; Wong et al., 1999). The growing number of national quality awards and publication of quality issues have proven that this strategy has been widely adopted.

This chapter reviews service quality concepts and applications. At the same time, it provides an introductory treatment of the SERVQUAL dimensions and gaps. SERVQUAL is a model that has been widely used in service quality analysis. The relationship between SERVQUAL and QFD techniques will be discussed. The importance and necessity of conducting service quality analysis are discussed also.

SERVICE QUALITY CONCEPT

An awareness of the importance of service quality to the survival of a company in this competitive world has started to spread to more and more companies. Crosby (1979) and others estimated the costs of poor quality to be about 30 to 40 percent of turnover. The number of companies with service quality as a performance measure is definitely increasing with the development of economies and the globalization of quality services.

According to Rust and Oliver (1994), service quality is by nature a subjective concept, which means that understanding how customers think about service quality is essential to effective management. Customer satisfaction, service quality, and customer value are three related concepts that are crucial to this understanding. Service quality is different from customer satisfaction in terms of form and dimension. Service quality is a form of long-run overall evaluation, whereas customer satisfaction is a transaction-specific measurement. In addition, service quality, is a function of the gap between perceived and desired or adequate service level. Unlike service quality, customer satisfaction is a function of the gap between perceived and predicted service level. While experience is not required to build perception in service quality, customer satisfaction is purely experiential. Furthermore, the dimensions underlying service quality judgments are specifically quality related. Satisfaction judgments, however, can result from any dimension, whether or not quality related. In contrast with service quality and customer satisfaction, customer value is formed by perceived quality in combination with price.

To deliver high value-added services, service companies need to increase their level of service capabilities as well as quality. In response to a perceived difference between product and service quality, Parasuraman et al. (1985) and Zeithaml et al. (1990) created a measurement of service quality, called SERVQUAL, from data on a number of services. Instead of analyzing objective quality, they used perceived quality and made comparisons between expectations and perceived performance. On the other hand, rather than relying on previous dimensions of product quality, they suggested 10 dimensions of service quality. Later empirical verification designed 22 items categorized into five dimensions to measure service quality. The dimensions are tangibles, reliability, responsiveness, assurance, and empathy.

Taylor et al. (1993) later stated two needs for developing SERVQUAL. One is the need for new knowledge in service quality, and the other is the need to have service quality measurements that include service characteristics (intangibility, heterogeneity, and inseparability, for example) in order to develop a full understanding of service quality. SERVQUAL researchers hypothesized that customers offer expectations on the service dimensions, and later form performance perceptions. These two key concepts are then compared through difference scores, or so-called "gaps." By examining the gaps between the expectation and perception scores, the objective of the SERVQUAL instrument becomes more evident, as does the meaning of service quality. Thus, the SERVQUAL instrument illustrates the core of what service quality may mean, namely a comparison to excellence in service as defined by the customer (Rust and Oliver, 1994).

Service Quality Dimensions

Research conducted by Parasuraman et al. in 1985 identified 10 dimensions that estimate service quality. Ninety-seven items were generated reflecting different dimensions. The dimensions were (Zeithaml et al., 1990)

1. *Tangible*: the physical environment in which the service is presented

2. *Reliability*: the consistency of performance and dependability

3. *Responsiveness*: the willingness to help the customer

4. *Competence*: the possession of the required skills and knowledge to perform the service

5. *Courtesy*: the supplier's behavior (for example, politeness, consideration, and kindness)

6. *Credibility*: trustworthiness, believability, and honesty of the service provider

7. *Security*: freedom from danger, risk, and doubt

8. *Access*: the ease of making contact with the supplier

9. *Communication*: the ability of talking in a way that is understandable to the customer

10. *Empathy*: the interest and possibility of becoming acquainted with the role of the customer

Many of these dimensions are related to the customers' confidence in those providing the service. The customer assessment of service quality can be reflected in these 10 dimensions (see Figure 8.1).

During the development of SERVQUAL, Zeithaml et al. (1990) found that some of the above-mentioned 10 dimensions were strongly correlated. As a result, the number of dimensions was reduced to the following 5:

1. *Tangibles*: physical facilities, equipments, and appearance of personnel

2. *Reliability*: ability to perform the promised service dependably and accurately

3. *Responsiveness*: willingness to help customers and to provide prompt service

4. *Assurance*: knowledge and courtesy of employees and the ability to convey trust and confidence

5. *Empathy*: caring, individualized attention that an organization provides to its customers

Most investigations using SERVQUAL have identified that reliability is by far the most important of these dimensions and that tangibles is the least important. The other three dimensions have approximately the same level of importance for a wide range of service industries (Bergman, 1994). However, the conclusion should not be simply generalized to other cases. In specific cases, the number and definition of quality dimensions have to be carefully thought over again (Carman, 1990).

The Gap Model for Service Quality

Zeithaml et al. (1990) discussed a model explaining causes of customer dissatisfaction. Called the Gap model, it is illustrated in Figure 8.2.

The SERVQUAL score is given by the equation:

$$Q = \frac{1}{22} \sum_{i=1}^{22} (P_i - E_i)$$

where

Q = Perceived service quality

P_i = Performance level perceived on attribute i for the delivered service

E_i = Expected performance level on attribute i for the service generated

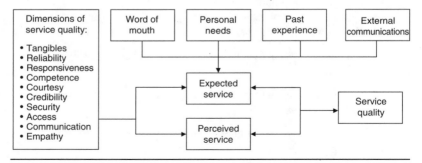

Figure 8.1   Customer assessment of service quality as described in Zeithaml et al. (1990). Used with permission.

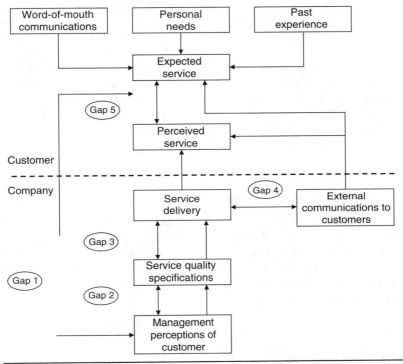

Figure 8.2 The Gap model developed by Zeithaml et al. (1990). Used with permission.

Equal weightings of the different attributes are assumed here. If a specific application indicates that different weightings are more appropriate, the equation above can be slightly adjusted to fit the situation by adding weight to the attributes. For example, if all three variables (importance, perception, and expectation) are material, and all play different roles in evaluating overall quality, it can be written as (Carman, 1990):

$$Q = \sum I_i \left(P_i - E_i \right)$$

where I_i is the importance of service attribute i.

Brief introductions to the five gaps that cause unsuccessful service delivery are presented next. Users can refer to Zeithaml et al. (1990) for a more detailed discussion. Several gaps can be bridged through more effective use of marketing research techniques.

Gap 1: Between customers' expectation and management's perceptions of these expectations. This gap consists of the discrepancies that arise because managers do not understand what customers consider to be of high quality. Knowing what customers want and expect is the very first step in delivering service quality. To be able to provide services that customers perceive as excellent, a firm has to know what its customers expect. Because services have fewer clearly defined and tangible quality dimensions, Gap 1 is in general considerably larger in service companies than it is in manufacturing firms. Some reasons for this gap are:

- Lack of marketing research

- Inadequate upward communication

- Too many levels of management

Gap 2: Between management's perceptions of customers' expectations and service quality specifications. This is a rather wide gap in many companies. Known customer expectations cannot be matched or exceeded because of difficulties in responding consistently to consumer demands and because of the absence of top management's commitment to service quality. Some reasons for this gap are:

- Inadequate management commitment to service quality

- Perception of unfeasibility

- Inadequate task standardization

- Absence of goal setting

Gap 3: Between service quality specifications and service delivery. Sometimes management really does understand customers' expectations and does set appropriate specifications, and yet the service delivered by the organization does not reach the customers' expectations. The difference between service specifications and the actual service delivery is the service-performance gap caused by employees who are unable or unwilling to perform the services at the desired level. Even when service guidelines exist, there may be a large variability in employee performance.

Some reasons for this gap may be:

- Role ambiguity

- Role conflict

- Poor employee job fit

- Poor technology job fit

- Inappropriate supervisory control systems

- Lack of perceived control

- Lack of teamwork

Gap 4: Between service delivery and external communications to customers about service delivery. This gap appears between what the firm promises about a service and what it actually delivers. Accurate and appropriate company communication, advertising, and public relations that do not overpromise or misrepresent are essential to delivering services that customers perceive as high in quality. It is important to realize that customer expectations are affected by media advertising and other forms of communication. Because people cannot be controlled in a way that machines can be controlled to produce more physical goods, the potential for overpromising may be higher for services.

Some reasons for this gap are:

- Inadequate horizontal communication among operations, marketing, and human resources, for example, among advertising, sales people, and operations

- Propensity for overpromising

The result of these four gaps is a fifth gap:

Gap 5: Between customers' expectation and perceived services. A good service quality is one that matches or exceeds customer expectations. Judgments of high and low service quality depend on how consumers perceive the actual service performance in the context of what is expected.

SERVQUAL VERSUS QFD

The benefits of SERVQUAL can be summarized as follows:

1. It is useful in understanding the opinion of customers regarding a service delivery, for example, perception, expectation, and satisfaction.

2. The model alerts management to consider expectations and perceptions by both internal and external customers.

3. The gaps among different people, and at different time periods regarding expectations and perceptions, can be identified.

4. It is useful in identifying specific areas of weaknesses and dissatisfaction.

5. It helps prioritize areas of service weakness to focus effort on.

6. It provides benchmarking analysis for organizations in the same service sector.

7. It can work as a basis for gathering customer requirements to explore further quality improvement analysis.

8. It can be combined with other quality techniques, such as QFD, to make a more complete quality improvement framework.

For the SERVQUAL model, its link to QFD lies in its effectiveness in identifying customer requirements in a robust way. A study by Curry and Herbert (1998) demonstrated the relevance to quality measurement of the SERVQUAL model and QFD, and showed the interlinking of these two approaches. The links can be reflected as shown in Figure 8.3.

The links can be further described as follows:

1. Customer expectation scores for individual requirements in SERVQUAL can be used to rank customer requirements in the HOQ.

2. Customer requirements identified in QFD contribute to design component questions in the expectation section of SERVQUAL.

3. Customer perception scores for individual requirements in SERVQUAL can be used to undertake a competitive benchmark analysis in the HOQ.

With SERVQUAL measuring both customer expectations and perceptions, and QFD translating these results and measurements into corresponding solutions, quality improvement and customer satisfaction can be

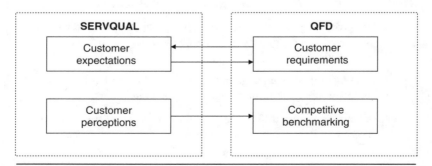

Figure 8.3 SERVQUAL versus QFD.

assured by delivering what is expected, and at the same time helping define strategic planning processes. Thus, although in general they are separate quality techniques, both with the objective of achieving greater customer satisfaction, the two techniques can in fact be integrated and linked to make better analyses and give greater contribution to the company.

INTEGRATION OF KANO'S MODEL, SERVQUAL, AND QFD

The Need to Integrate QFD with SERVQUAL

A practical approach to improving SERVQUAL is to develop or design action plans that will lead to the improvement of attribute performance. It is imperative to know that the gap between predicted service and perceived service exists. But it is more important to find ways to close the gap. Berry et al. (1994) suggested the following five plans for closing the gap of service attributes:

1. Defining the service roles

2. Competing for talent

3. Emphasizing service teams

4. Going for reliability

5. Being great at problem resolution

Some lessons learned for improving service quality can be found in Kuei and Lu (1997). These "golden rules," however, are not sufficient. Organizations need a clear-cut tool to guide their improvement efforts. Thus, there is a need to develop an approach that can bridge the result of the periodic measurement, and a pragmatic way for improvement.

QFD is a planning process for translating customer needs into appropriate organization requirements at every stage of a product's life cycle, from research to sales to service. Through the HOQ, QFD shows all the information to help the organization set targets or determine the priority of action that need to be taken. The main goal of QFD is to increase customer satisfaction by improving an organization's attribute performance and by exciting the customer through innovation (Lee et al., 2000).

By integrating SERVQUAL into QFD, an organization is able to:

- Provide a basis for designing the improvement planning process

- Ensure that the service can meet the customer needs

- Highlight and prioritize key action plans in order to ensure the success of implementation

- Allocate the resources efficiently

- Enhance documentation, communication, and teamwork

A Framework to Integrate Kano's Model, SERVQUAL, and QFD

In linking SERVQUAL and QFD, Kuei and Lu (1997) assigned the gap scores, which result from SERVQUAL, as the importance ratings in the HOQ. The rationale behind this step is that the larger the gap, the higher the priority for improvement. However, using the gap as the importance rating is not sufficient to develop the priorities. The relationship between customer satisfaction and attribute performance needs to be considered, otherwise the improvement effort may be in vain. To solve this problem, therefore, the present research does not only integrate SERVQUAL and QFD, it also involves the Kano model.

Figure 8.4 proposes a detailed framework that illustrates how Kano's model and QFD can be integrated into SERVQUAL to ensure the design of improvement planning. The first step is to develop the Kano categories parameter. This Kano parameter can be established by QFD practitioners. The establishment of these values is based on the implications of Kano's model.

In the Kano model, a slight improvement to attributes within the attractive category may result in a large increase in customer satisfaction. Within the one-dimensional category, the increase in customer satisfaction is linearly proportional to improvement in the attributes. However, for the must-be category, the level of customer satisfaction will never increase beyond neutral, no matter how great the improvement to these attributes.

The above implies that values assigned to the parameters of the Kano categories should be in descending order, with the largest value assigned to the attractive category and the smallest to the must-be category. Shen (2000) adopted the values "4", "2", and "1" for the attractive, one-dimensional, and must-be categories, respectively, in his case study.

The second step is to calculate the adjusted importance level. This adjusted level is the core of the integration of Kano's model, SERVQUAL, and QFD. It is calculated by multiplying the Kano category parameter and the tourist satisfaction score. The involvement of the Kano model in the

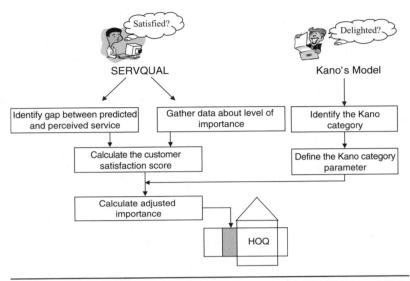

Figure 8.4 Framework of the integration of Kano's Model, SERVQUAL, and QFD.

integration of SERVQUAL and QFD is to ensure that high customer satisfaction is achieved.

To achieve total customer satisfaction in an effective way, an organization should not only know what customers want most, but also understand how much effort should be put to each customer attribute in order to achieve the desired customer satisfaction level. The predicted service score that results from SERVQUAL measurement, therefore, is useful to be employed as the target value in the HOQ. Without using the predicted service score as the target value, possibly the customer will not be satisfied with a certain service attribute or maybe the customer satisfaction target will be overfulfilled.

Given the Kano category characteristics, the overfulfilled target is a must when the attributes belong to attractive and one-dimensional categories, but not when it belongs to the must-be category. Neglect of the target value and of the Kano category may not result in total customer satisfaction. In short, this proposed approach offers three main issues that organizations should be concerned about: determining the appropriate Kano parameter value, utilizing the adjusted importance level, and further employing the predicted service score as the target of the attributes.

Chapter 9

Some Advanced QFD Implementation Issues

Although we have presented several approaches with regard to the advanced QFD applications in this book, the focus has been on the analysis of HOQ information and quantitative studies. When QFD is implemented, there are many other related issues, some of which are discussed here. They have not been extensively discussed in the literature and would benefit from further research.

We first consider the case of when a product is to be designed for different customer groups, which is common today. *Different customer groups might have different needs.* It is important to deal with these needs, either separately by designing different products to tailor to them, or by using a proper weightage, so that the average needs will be met. A second problem occurs when customers express the needs in qualitative terms. This is especially the case when service quality is to be improved. Finally, we consider the case of when the developed HOQ has become very large. In that case, a systematic reduction approach might be useful.

USING QFD FOR SEGMENTED CUSTOMER GROUPS

In the traditional HOQ, there is only one customer group. In this case, we can easily find the corresponding engineering characteristics for the design of the product or service. However, it is common for a company to have more than one customer group with different requirements for the same product. Meeting the requirements of one customer group does not mean that the product can be accepted by other customer groups. If the different customer groups have similar requirements for the same product and the importance of the requirements is almost the same, traditional QFD can be applied.

However, different customer groups sometimes focus on different aspects of the product characteristics, or maybe they even have totally different requirements for the same product. In order not to lose the customers and be able to remain competitive in the world market, most companies will set their targets as trying to satisfy as many customer groups as possible within their resource and feasibility constraints. When different customer groups have different requirements, the most ideal case is to develop different products to satisfy each customer group separately. However, this is usually impossible in the real world, as the companies are subject either to resource or technical constraints.

The Difficulties of Satisfying Multigroup Customers

The major concern of all companies is to know correctly what the customers really need. Failing to understand the customers' needs is an outrageously expensive way to develop products. By effectively estimating the customer requirements, companies will be allowed to envision what future products or process designs must be in order to stay competitive. It will also give a window on unit manufacturing costs and selling prices, and directions for R&D efforts and budgeting.

An attractive feature of QFD is the focus on the VOCs. Correctly understanding the customer requirements is the most important step toward greater customer satisfaction. It is a common practice when there are several customer groups for a company. In this case, it is more complicated—and more important—to identify the real customer needs and find a way to satisfy all of the customer groups. For one product, such as a wallet, people with high salaries and positions may want the wallet to be made of expensive leather and look luxurious, whereas people with low salaries and positions may want it to be durable and cheap.

On the other hand, there may also be cases where *not all of the customers are end users.* VOCs may include the demands of regulators, the needs of retailers, the requirements of vendors, and so forth. All of these different groups of customers may have their own requirements for the same product, which are reflected either by the differences of the VOC items or by the differences of the importance for the VOCs in the HOQ given by the different groups. Therefore, as different customer groups may either have different or conflicting needs for the same product, how to satisfy all of the customer groups becomes a major concern of many companies.

The HOQ is generally used to relate the VOCs to the engineering characteristics. In the traditional HOQ, there is only one customer group. However, since it is quite common for a company to have more than one customer group for a particular product, approaches to solving multigroup VOCs become urgent and necessary. At the same time, whether to develop one product to maximize the satisfaction of several customer groups, to develop several different products, or to use other decision rules becomes a major concern for most decision makers.

If all of the customer groups are very important to the company and their requirements are very representative, failing to meet their requirements may cause considerable loss of profit for the company. In this situation, the company may elect to develop several different products to satisfy different customer groups separately, especially when they have conflicting quality requirements. However, in the real world, there may be strict resource constraints that make the developing of several products either impossible or unprofitable. Thus, if the requirements of different customer groups do not greatly differ, the company may elect to develop only one product (using the weighted averages of the VOCs) to satisfy all customers, or at least to satisfy the most important customer group. The limited resources can then be made the best of.

Generally, the decision maker may select one of the following three decision rules for conflicting customer requirements:

1. Satisfy the most important customer group.

2. Develop different products to satisfy different customer groups.

3. Use the weighted average of the importance of VOC items as the overall importance of VOCs.

In the following, details of the decision rule for the nonconflicting customer groups and the three decision rules for the conflicting customer groups are discussed. How to use the HOQ in each case is then presented, with the advantages and disadvantages of each of the decision rules addressed.

Decision Rule for Nonconflicting Customer Groups

Even though there are several different customer groups for the company, their requirements for the same product may be quite similar, or even the same. In this case, we can regard all of the customer groups as one customer group. The whole problem then becomes a problem that can be directly solved by one HOQ.

An Illustrative Example

A fictitious company named Backpacking is designing a tourist camp stove, as described in Thurston and Locascio (1993). After adequate training, the president formed a committee composed of professionals from engineering, manufacturing, sales, and marketing. The team is named Backpack. The team asked three representative customer groups what they needed and what they expected to get from this product. The customer groups were then asked to brainstorm all the needs and wants they had regarding the new product, and to give each of these needs a relative importance.

Suppose the results of the VOCs and their normalized importance to the customers are shown in Table 9.1.

From Table 9.1, we can draw the conclusion that the three customer groups have 11 nonconflicting requirements. The importance of the requirements is the same for customer group 1 and customer group 2. The only differences for customer group 3 from the other two customer groups are the

Table 9.1   VOCs and their importance.

VOCs	Importance to customer group 1	Importance to customer group 2	Importance to customer group 3
Very compact	0.06	0.06	0.06
Weighs little	0.05	0.05	0.05
Lights easily	0.03	0.03	0.03
Very stable	0.40	0.04	0.04
Operates quietly	0.02	0.02	0.02
Heats quickly	0.06	0.06	0.06
No repair needed	0.01	0.01	0.02
Can simmer	0.02	0.02	0.01
Burns long with least weight	0.02	0.02	0.02
Refillable	0.22	0.22	0.22
Gas-ready available	0.12	0.12	0.12

importance of "No repair needed" (0.02) and "Can simmer" (0.01). Since these two requirements are not very important compared to other requirements, the decision maker may then decide to use the importance of the requirements of the first two customer groups as the overall importance of the VOCs.

These VOC items were then translated into technical features by the engineers. In total, 11 technical features were identified to meet the customer requirements. The problem can then be solved directly by one HOQ, as shown in Figure 9.1.

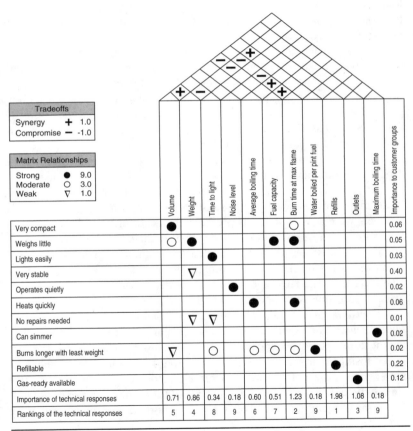

Figure 9.1 The HOQ for nonconflicting customer groups.

Decision Rules for Conflicting Customer Groups

The method of solving nonconflicting customer groups is very straightforward and simple, whereas in the real world, it is more common for the different customer groups to have different requirements for the same product, or for the importance of the requirements of different customer groups to differ significantly. In such situations, the decision maker will have to choose a decision rule. Benefit-cost and feasibility will become the major concerns of the company. The following are the three decision rules that may be elected by the company.

Decision Rule 1: Satisfy the most important customer group. In this case, different customer groups have different requirements of the same product, but developing several kinds of products to satisfy each of the customer groups is either not possible or not profitable for the company. Then, the company may choose to satisfy the most important customer group instead of satisfying all of the customer groups.

The advantage of this decision rule is that the company will not lose its most important customers, and it can still retain the major part of its market share. At the same time, developing only one product to satisfy the most important customer group is generally feasible and affordable for a company. However, since not all of the customers are satisfied, the company may risk the loss of its potential customers, even though they are not currently the most important group of customers.

As an illustrative example, suppose the three customer groups have different requirements of the tourist camp stove, as shown in Table 9.2.

After the analysis, the company found that customer group 2 was the most important customer group, since about 60 percent of the company's products were sold to this group of customers. In order to keep this customer group, the decision makers decided to generate a product with the purpose of satisfying this particular customer group. Then, the 10 VOC items that were needed by the second customer group were used in the HOQ analysis. The HOQ for the most important customer group (customer group 2) was thus developed. This is shown in Figure 9.2.

Decision Rule 2: Develop different products to satisfy different customer groups. Although sometimes the decision maker may elect to satisfy the most important customer group, the company will have to face the danger of losing some of its other customer groups. Although these other customer groups are not the most important customer groups at present, the sum of them may take a very large portion of the total number of customers, and some of them may even become very important potential customers of the company in the future.

Table 9.2 VOCs and their importance.

VOCs	Importance to customer group 1	Importance to customer group 2	Importance to customer group 3
Very compact	0.06	0.05	0.20
Weighs little	0.05	0.04	0.05
Lights easily	0.03	0.07	0.10
Very stable	0.40	0.50	
Operates quietly		0.05	0.25
Heats quickly	0.08	0.02	0.20
No repairs needed	0.03	0.20	
Can simmer	0.02	0.02	0.01
Burns long with least weight			0.02
Refillable	0.22	0.01	
Gas-ready available	0.11	0.04	0.17

In this case, the company may elect to use one HOQ to develop different products with different characteristics to satisfy different customer groups. The obvious advantage of this election is that the company will not lose its customers, although in practice the company may have certain cost and technical constraints that may hinder the development of several products.

For the requirements of the three customer groups which are shown in Table 9.2, if the company elects to generate three products to meet different customer needs separately, one HOQ, as shown in Figure 9.3, can be used with different rankings of the engineering characteristics for each customer group. The company can then use the importance and ranking of the engineering characteristics for customer group 1 to develop one product to satisfy customer group 1. The importance and rankings of the engineering characteristics for the other two customer groups can be used to develop another two products to satisfy the other two customer groups separately.

Decision Rule 3: Use the weighted average of the VOCs as the overall VOC. Since both the decision to satisfy the most important customer group and the decision to satisfy different customer groups separately have their own advantages and disadvantages, sometimes the decision maker may

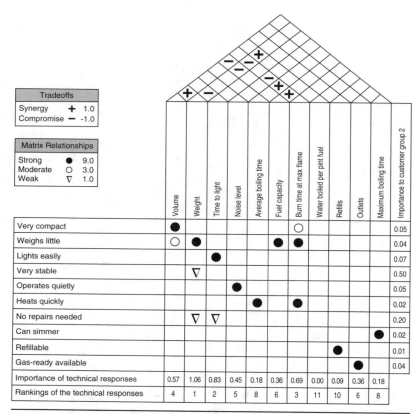

Figure 9.2 The HOQ for the most important customer group.

elect to adopt a decision rule between the two. By giving each customer group a relative weight for their importance as a customer group to the company, the company can use the weighted averages of the importance of the VOCs as the overall importance.

Since there are several customer groups, we can use the weighted averages of the importance of VOCs as the importance of the overall VOC in the HOQ. If different customer groups have different requirement items of the same product, we can simply add all the requirement items to the column of VOC. The difference of the requirements by different customer groups can also be reflected by the importance they give to each VOC item.

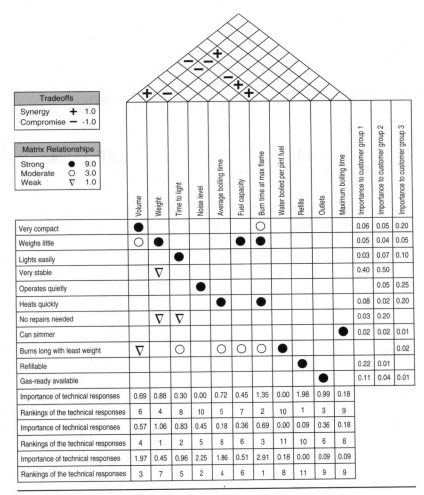

	Volume	Weight	Time to light	Noise level	Average boiling time	Fuel capacity	Burn time at max flame	Water boiled per pint fuel	Refills	Outlets	Maximum boiling time	Importance to customer group 1	Importance to customer group 2	Importance to customer group 3
Very compact	●							O				0.06	0.05	0.20
Weighs little	O	●				●	●					0.05	0.04	0.05
Lights easily			●									0.03	0.07	0.10
Very stable				▽								0.40	0.50	
Operates quietly					●								0.05	0.25
Heats quickly					●		●					0.08	0.02	0.20
No repairs needed				▽	▽							0.03	0.20	
Can simmer											●	0.02	0.02	0.01
Burns long with least weight	▽		O		O	O	O	●						0.02
Refillable									●			0.22	0.01	
Gas-ready available										●		0.11	0.04	0.01
Importance of technical responses	0.69	0.88	0.30	0.00	0.72	0.45	1.35	0.00	1.98	0.99	0.18			
Rankings of the technical responses	6	4	8	10	5	7	2	10	1	3	9			
Importance of technical responses	0.57	1.06	0.83	0.45	0.18	0.36	0.69	0.00	0.09	0.36	0.18			
Rankings of the technical responses	4	1	2	5	8	6	3	11	10	6	8			
Importance of technical responses	1.97	0.45	0.96	2.25	1.86	0.51	2.91	0.18	0.00	0.09	0.09			
Rankings of the technical responses	3	7	5	2	4	6	1	8	11	9	9			

Tradeoffs
Synergy + 1.0
Compromise − -1.0

Matrix Relationships
Strong ● 9.0
Moderate O 3.0
Weak ▽ 1.0

Figure 9.3   The HOQ for different customer groups.

Suppose c_{ij} is the importance of the ith VOC given by the jth customer group, and the importance of the jth customer group to the company is w_j, the weighted average of the ith VOC is then:

$$c_{i1}w_1 + c_{i2}w_2 + \ldots + c_{ij}w_j \tag{9.1}$$

This weighted average of the ith VOC is then used in the HOQ to get the ranking and the importance of the engineering characteristics.

For the tourist camp stove problem and the three customer groups, one HOQ can be used to get the overall importance and ranking of the engineering characteristics. As the purpose of this illustrative example is to show the procedure of solving the problem, we simply regard these three customer groups as equally important to the company in this example. Different weightings, however, should be applied in real-world applications if needed. The HOQ is shown in Figure 9.4.

IMPLEMENTATION OF QFD BASED ON LINGUISTIC DATA

It has been recognized that the relationship matrix plays an important role in mapping the voice of the customer onto the voice of the engineer. The

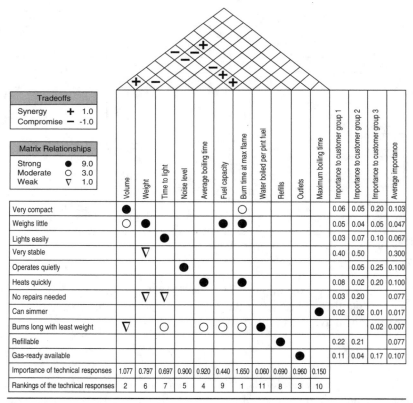

	Volume	Weight	Time to light	Noise level	Average boiling time	Fuel capacity	Burn time at max flame	Water boiled per pint fuel	Refills	Outlets	Maximum boiling time	Importance to customer group 1	Importance to customer group 2	Importance to customer group 3	Average importance
Very compact	●						○					0.06	0.05	0.20	0.103
Weighs little	○	●				●	●					0.05	0.04	0.05	0.047
Lights easily			●									0.03	0.07	0.10	0.067
Very stable			▽									0.40	0.50		0.300
Operates quietly				●									0.05	0.25	0.100
Heats quickly					●		●					0.08	0.02	0.20	0.100
No repairs needed		▽	▽									0.03	0.20		0.077
Can simmer											●	0.02	0.02	0.01	0.017
Burns long with least weight	▽		○		○	○	○	●					0.02		0.007
Refillable									●			0.22	0.21		0.077
Gas-ready available										●		0.11	0.04	0.17	0.107
Importance of technical responses	1.077	0.797	0.697	0.900	0.920	0.440	1.650	0.060	0.690	0.960	0.150				
Rankings of the technical responses	2	6	7	5	4	9	1	11	8	3	10				

Tradeoffs
Synergy + 1.0
Compromise − -1.0

Matrix Relationships
Strong ● 9.0
Moderate ○ 3.0
Weak ▽ 1.0

Figure 9.4 The HOQ for Method 1.

use of a more level relationship system should be able to help QFD users differentiate relationships between customer attributes and technical characteristics. However, from a decision-making point of view, it may be easier for decision makers to utilize quantitative rather than qualitative information. In the case of QFD, there is often an issue of quantifying various inputs, such as the importance of each attribute that customers perceive and relationships that QFD users estimate.

The QFD process involves various inputs in the form of linguistic data (human perception, judgment, and evaluation on importance of customer requirements or relationship strength, for example), which are usually subjective and uncertain. However, in the traditional QFD analysis, most of these input variables are assumed to be precise and treated as numerical data. To make it intuitive and more meaningful, the *vagueness and ambiguity inherent in the linguistic input* may be treated mathematically with the help of fuzzy set theory.

Some progress has been made along these lines. Masud and Dean (1993) reported an investigation of how QFD analysis could be performed when the input variables are treated as linguistic variables with values expressed as fuzzy numbers. Bahrami (1994) introduced a method for performing routine design by using information content and fuzzy QFD based on the concept of linguistic variable. Kim et al. (1997) presented an integrated approach that allows a design team to consider the tradeoffs among various customer attributes as well as the inherent fuzziness in the system. Fung et al. (1998) proposed a hybrid system that incorporates the principles of QFD, AHP, and fuzzy set theory to tackle the complex and often imprecise problem domain encountered in customer requirement management. Nevertheless, it can be seen from the above that more systematic procedures need to be studied and developed for the successful use of QFD in a fuzzy environment.

In addition, when implementing QFD with linguistic data, some factors may affect the results of QFD, for example, the ranking of technical characteristics, the type of fuzzy numbers, which defuzzification strategies are used, and the degree of fuzziness of the fuzzy numbers. Little research has been done on which factors would have an influence on the results, and to what extent. However, knowing this information is essential for the successful use of the fuzzy approach.

As a consequence, one objective here is to propose a fuzzy process model that can be easily integrated into the traditional QFD process. This model would have the ability to consider the two main inputs of QFD (the importance to customer and relationship strength) as linguistic variables. It is intended to produce the results in the form of either fuzzy or crisp numbers, depending on varying requests. Another objective is to examine the ability of two important factors that affect the ranking of technical characteristics. They are defuzzification strategies and the degree of fuzziness of fuzzy numbers. While other related factors, such as type of fuzzy numbers and number of fuzzy numbers, are not included here, their effects can be easily considered in a similar manner.

Linguistic Data in QFD

Most of the input data in QFD operations and activities are linguistic and in a natural language. For example, customer requirements are often vague and loosely stated, such as "easy to use," "safe," and "comfortable." Capturing the elasticity of imprecise requirements is an important issue (Liu and Yen, 1996). Simonson (1993) stated that customers' preferences are often fuzzy and imprecise, for example, "very important" and "somewhat important." In addition, the relationships between customer attributes and technical characteristics are also identified in a qualitative way (Belhe and Kusiak, 1996), and they are ambiguous in nature, for example, "strong relationship." Thus, it may be more appropriate to treat these inputs as fuzzy rather than precise, since linguistic data may not be easily quantified and incorporated into the QFD process.

Fuzzy set theory was developed for solving problems in which descriptions of activities and observations are imprecise, vague, and uncertain. It provides a strict mathematical framework in which vague conceptual phenomena can be precisely and rigorously studied. It is primarily concerned with quantifying the vagueness in human thought, cognition, and perception. Applying fuzzy set theory, the transition from vagueness to quantification can be performed.

To deal with the description about the vagueness of an object, Zadeh (1965) proposed a membership function associated with each object in the form of a grade of membership belonging to the interval [0,1]. A fuzzy set is designated as: $\forall x \in X$, $\mu_A(x) \in [0,1]$, where $\mu_A(x)$ is the degree of membership, ranging from 0 to 1, of a vague predicate, A, over the universe of objects, X. X is a space set which can be real numbers, natural numbers, or integers. The membership function can be viewed as an opinion poll of human thoughts and perceptions, or as expert opinion.

A linguistic variable differs from a numerical variable in that its values are not numbers but words or phrases in some language (Zadeh, 1975). The use of linguistic variables allows a precise modeling of an imprecise statement, such as "very important" or "somewhat important." The successful use of linguistic variables is highly dependent on the determination of a valid membership function. Arithmetic operations can be performed on linguistic variables represented as fuzzy numbers, which is a normal and convex fuzzy set with membership function that satisfies both normality and convexity (Kaufmann and Gupta, 1985).

A process model for implementing QFD under a fuzzy environment is developed in the following section. Particularly, fuzzification of the input data and defuzzification of the output data are presented. A further section presents an example illustrating the use of this proposed fuzzy QFD model. Sensitivity analysis is given before concluding this chapter.

A Process Model for QFD with Linguistic Input

As described earlier, the QFD process requires various input data, which are fuzzy and vague in nature, and hence are better represented as linguistic variables. To implement QFD based on linguistic data, a process model including the use of the concepts of linguistic variable, fuzzy number, fuzzy arithmetic, and defuzzification, is proposed in this section (see Figure 9.5).

Step 0: Initialization. This step is basically concerned with the preparation of the QFD project. Several issues are involved in this step, including deciding the purpose of the QFD study (a new version, upgrade, or cost reduction); defining the expected benefits; selecting the product or service to be studied; forming the QFD team (such as people from R&D, engineering, manufacturing, marketing, finance, and customer service); and if necessary, training the team members.

Step 1: Identification of linguistic data. In this step, QFD team members collect customer requirements through brainstorming, focus groups, customer surveys, and other techniques. After customer requirements have been substantially identified and developed, customers are asked to make their judgments on the importance of each requirement. They may rank and categorize the customer requirements into several groups, each of which falls into one of several importance levels. After coming up with the technical characteristics, QFD team members identify the relationships between customer attributes and technical characteristics.

The difference between the proposed model and traditional QFD in this step is that these data are expressed and represented as linguistic variables rather than as crisp numbers. For example, for the importance of customer attribute "interesting Web pages," instead of using the traditional numerical scale (1–5 scale, for example), customers may be asked to rank this requirement as not important at all, or very important, or perhaps others. For the strength of relationships between customer attributes and technical characteristics, QFD team members may categorize them into weak, moderate, or strong, rather than the traditional numerical scale, for example [1 3 9]. It should be more intuitive and easier for them to identify the input data in a natural language, rather than as an exact numerical value.

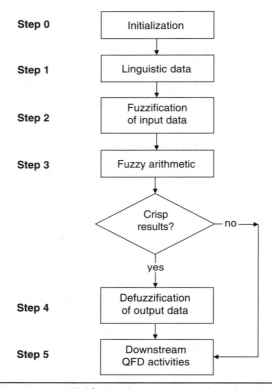

Figure 9.5   A process model for implementing QFD based on linguistic data.

Step 2: Fuzzification of input data. The input data are identified in the form of linguistic variables in the previous step. They are further represented as fuzzy numbers in step 2. In this process model, two important input data are treated as linguistic variables and fuzzified into fuzzy numbers, namely, the importance of customer requirements and the strength of relationship between customer attributes and technical characteristics.

The importance to customers is expressed as linguistic variables (not important at all, somewhat important, moderately important, important, and very important), which can be further converted into fuzzy numbers. One possible set of membership functions for these fuzzy numbers can be found in Figure 9.6. Note that the use of these simple membership functions is for illustrative purposes and, thus, may not represent the exact one used in practice. In the following, the triangular fuzzy number is used for simplicity, and all membership functions for linguistic input data are standardized over the interval [0,1].

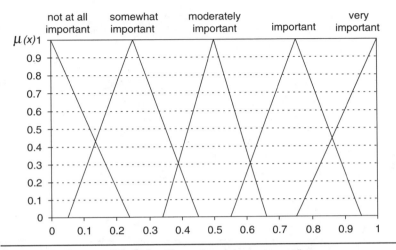

Figure 9.6 Fuzzy numbers for "importance to customer."

The relationship matrix indicates how much each technical character-istic affects each customer attribute. To numerically map the voice of the customer onto the voice of the engineer, two scales are traditionally adopted, for example [1 3 5] and [1 3 9]. Occasionally other scales are used. As mentioned earlier, the literature, however, does not document any basis for choosing either value set (Sivaloganathan and Evbuomwan, 1997). The weighing scheme representing the relationship strength is subjective and rather arbitrary (Kim, 1997).

To cope with these difficulties, linguistic variables help QFD practition-ers categorize relationships intuitively. In step 1, the relationship strengths are judged as either none, weak, moderate, or strong, which can be further rep-resented by fuzzy numbers. Figure 9.7 shows one possible set of fuzzy num-bers for relationship strength, with membership functions plotted.

Step 3: Applying fuzzy arithmetic. Fuzzy arithmetic, which is a direct application of the extension principle, can be used on fuzzy numbers. In this step, fuzzy arithmetic is applied to the calculation of the priorities of the technical characteristics, for instance, the relative contribution of the technical characteristics to overall customer satisfaction. The technical pri-ority is a key result of QFD since it guides QFD practitioners in decision making, resource allocation, and the subsequent QFD phases. The addition and multiplication of fuzzy numbers will be performed for the calculation of the technical priorities. Specifically, for each technical characteristic, its priority can be obtained by adding all the weighted relationships in the

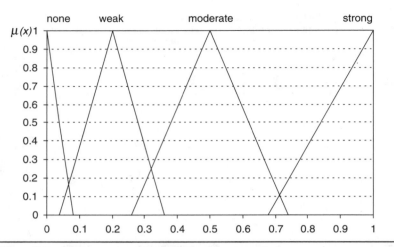

Figure 9.7 Fuzzy numbers for "relationship strength."

form of fuzzy numbers, each of which is calculated by multiplying the relationship strength by the importance of the corresponding customer attribute.

Step 4: Defuzzification of output data. In this process model, one decision needs to be made by the QFD team members. They should decide which type of output data is more useful and easy to interpret, for example, whether crisp or fuzzy results are preferred. If fuzzy technical priorities are required, step 4 will be skipped and the process goes directly to step 5. On the other hand, if crisp output data are preferred, the fuzzy technical priority based on fuzzy arithmetic will be defuzzified into crisp results through step 4, and be further utilized in downstream QFD activities.

In the event that crisp results are required, defuzzification is performed to transform the fuzzy technical priorities into crisp output. Defuzzification is defined as a mapping of a fuzzy set A to elements of the universe considered significant with respect to A. Various defuzzification techniques have been suggested. For more information on defuzzification strategies and their selection, see Zhao and Govind (1991) and Runkler (1997).

In this chapter, two frequently used defuzzification methods are selected, namely, the Mean of Maxima (MOM) and the Centroid method. The MOM method selects a nonfuzzy output value corresponding to the maximum value of the membership function. The values are averaged when there is more than one such output value. This method results in the most probable solution, but it does not take into account the remaining information given by the fuzzy set.

The Centroid defuzzification method calculates the centroid or center of gravity (COG) of the area under the membership function $\mu_A(x)$. Let x^* denote the defuzzified value of fuzzy set A. The Centroid method can be defined by:

$$x^* = \frac{\int_X \mu_A(x) \cdot x\, dx}{\int_X \mu_A(x)\, dx} \tag{9.2}$$

Unlike the MOM method, the Centroid method makes a compromise between all possible solutions, but it does not generally choose the most likely solution.

Step 5: Downstream QFD activities. In this step, the subsequent activities and operations involved in the QFD process are implemented based on the preceding steps. Two possible situations can occur here. One is that the HOQ is the only phase used in the QFD process. In this case, downstream issues primarily include the interpretation of the information that HOQ provides. The other possibility is that the HOQ is the first phase of the whole QFD process, where parts deployment, process planning, and/or production planning may be incorporated into the subsequent activities.

This process model is based mainly on the HOQ. In other words, this model shows only the implementation process of HOQ under a fuzzy environment by using linguistic variables and fuzzy numbers. Nevertheless, the HOQ is the most commonly used matrix in QFD and it contains many of the features that can be seen in other parts of QFD. Thus, the fuzzy approach can be easily integrated into the HOQ and extended into the whole QFD process when necessary.

An Illustrative Example

To help illustrate the use of the proposed fuzzy approach in dealing with linguistic data when implementing QFD, an example is presented in this section (Shen et al., 2001). It focuses on the application of QFD in defining and designing good Web pages. The scenario of the example will be introduced, and the above process model will be applied to this example. A comparison between the fuzzy approach and the traditional one will also be addressed based on this example.

Scenario of the Example

QFD was employed to look into the human/user interface aspects of a Web page for quality improvement. An analysis of general customer requirements identified a list of needs for good Web pages, for example, "interesting Web page" and "good linkages." QFD team members further translated these requirements into technical characteristics, for example, "use of graphics" and "number of updated links." These customer requirements and technical characteristics are presented in the HOQ (see Figure 9.8). For simplicity, the roof part of the HOQ is not included.

Applying the Proposed Model

Following step 1, the importance of the customer need and the relationship strength were identified as linguistic data. As Table 9.1 shows, the customer requirements were categorized by using linguistic variables (very important, important, moderately important, or somewhat important). Similarly, the relationships between the customer requirements and the technical characteristics were linguistically judged as either none, weak, moderate, or strong.

Relationship Key

Strong	●	9.0
Moderate	○	3.0
Weak	▽	1.0
None		Blank

	Importance to Customer	H1: Use of graphics	H2: Amount of text and information	H3: Text formatting	H4: Spelling and grammar	H5: Standard page design	H6: Integration of links into text	H7: Provision of links for downloaded information	H8: Provision of link back to home page	H9: Organization of pages	H10: Number of updated links	H11: Size of page	H12: Speed of computers and communications
Interesting Web pages	important	●			▽								
Easy-to-read text	moderately		▽	●	○								
Uniform & standardized page design	some			▽		●			▽				
Sufficient information	moderately		●										
Easy-to-locate information	moderately						▽			●			
Good linkages	very							○	○		●		
Good integration of links	important						●	○					
Fast in loading	very	○	○									○	●
Technical importance (crisp)		1.32	1.21	0.72	0.49	0.87	0.87	1.06	0.67	0.66	0.99	0.67	0.99
Relative importance (%)		12.5	11.5	6.9	4.6	8.3	8.3	10.1	6.3	6.2	9.5	6.3	9.5
Technical ranking		1	2	8	12	6	6	3	9	11	4	9	4

Figure 9.8 The HOQ with linguistic inputs and defuzzified technical priorities.

These linguistic data were further converted into fuzzy numbers as previously described in step 2. The membership functions associated with the linguistic term "importance to customer" are defined as follows:

$$\mu_{very}(x) = \frac{1 - 10x}{3} \qquad 0 \leq x \leq 0.3$$

$$= 0 \qquad 0.3 \leq x \leq 1$$

$$\mu_{important}(x) = 4x \qquad 0 \leq x \leq 0.25$$

$$= 2 - 4x \qquad 0.25 \leq x \leq 0.5$$

$$= 0 \qquad 0.5 \leq x \leq 1$$

$$\mu_{moderately}(x) = 0 \qquad 0 \leq x \leq 0.3 \text{ and } 0.7 \leq x \leq 1$$

$$= 5x - 1.5 \qquad 0.3 \leq x \leq 0.5$$

$$= 3.5 - 5x \qquad 0.5 \leq x \leq 0.7$$

$$\mu_{some}(x) = 0 \qquad 0 \leq x \leq 0.5$$

$$= 4x - 2 \qquad 0.5 \leq x \leq 0.75$$

$$= 4 - 4x \qquad 0.75 \leq x \leq 0.1$$

$$\mu_{not}(x) = 0 \qquad 0 \leq x \leq 0.7$$

$$= \frac{10x}{3} - \frac{7}{3} \qquad 0.7 \leq x \leq 0.1$$

Similarly, the membership functions associated with the linguistic term "relationship strength" are defined as follows:

$$\mu_{none}(x) = 1 - 10x \qquad 0 \leq x \leq 0.1$$

$$= 0 \qquad 0.1 \leq x \leq 1$$

$$\mu_{weak}(x) = 5x \qquad 0 \leq x \leq 0.2$$

$$= 2 - 5x \qquad 0.2 \leq x \leq 0.4$$

$$= 0 \qquad 0.4 \leq x \leq 1$$

$$\mu_{moderate}(x) = 0 \qquad 0 \leq x \leq 0.2 \text{ and } 0.8 \leq x \leq 1$$

$$= \frac{10x}{3} - \frac{2}{3} \qquad 0.2 \leq x \leq 0.5$$

$$= \frac{8}{3} - \frac{10x}{3} \qquad 0.5 \leq x \leq 0.8$$

$$\mu_{strong}(x) = 0 \qquad\qquad 0 \leq x \leq 0.7$$

$$= 2.5x - 1.5 \qquad 0.7 \leq x \leq 1$$

Following step 3, the technical importance values were calculated by applying fuzzy arithmetic (multiplication and addition). In this example, we assume that the crisp results are required and the Centroid defuzzification strategy is used. The defuzzified technical importance, relative importance, and ranking of each technical characteristic are shown in Table 8.1. Results showed that among the identified technical characteristics, "use of graphics," "amount of text and information," and "provision of links for downloaded information" were the three most important features for satisfying customer needs (Shen et al., 2001).

SIZE REDUCTION OF LARGE HOQ

The Need for Size Reduction in HOQ

Although QFD is applied by many companies in a wide spectrum of fields, the success of QFD will be seriously affected when the size of the HOQ is too large. A widely recognized difficulty in the application of QFD is the large size of HOQ. A reasonable-sized HOQ with 20 VOCs and 30 Engineering characteristics (ECs) will have more than 1,000 relationships to be filled, which may lead to even more effort in the following phases of QFD analysis.

The complexity of QFD increases with size because of the impediments in interpreting the many interactions between VOCs and ECs, as well as the correlation of ECs. Many companies have faced the problem of large HOQ. The large size leads to the need for a large amount of time, effort, and cost to build the HOQ and to conduct the QFD analysis. Significant conclusions, on the other hand, may be difficult to obtain because of the confusing structure.

Therefore, there is an urgent need to develop a framework as guidance for QFD users to reduce the size of the HOQ, and hence obtain more effective and efficient HOQs. Hunter and Landingham (1994) suggested deleting items considered trivial. Kim et al. (1997) presented a formal approach to reduce the size of the HOQ chart by using the concept of design decomposition combined with multiattribute value theory. Shin and Kim (1997) employed factor analysis to restructure a given HOQ.

A general, cost-based framework was developed by Wang (2001) to reduce the size of an HOQ, while at the same time ensuring the satisfaction of customer requirements to an acceptable degree. The objective of an HOQ in meeting customer requirements is, therefore, not violated. The satisfaction level, on the other hand, is the key factor in our methodology for solving large HOQ problems. By fulfilling a certain level of customer requirements instead of 100 percent fulfillment, some engineering characteristics may be deemed redundant. The size of an HOQ, thus, can be reduced by eliminating some of the less useful engineering characteristics.

A Framework for Reducing the Size of an HOQ

The two most important parts of an HOQ are the VOCs and the ECs. The number of items in these two parts will eventually determine the size of an HOQ. Therefore, the size reduction of HOQ should be conducted from both directions. At the same time, as stated before, customer satisfaction as the objective of product design should not be undermined.

In order to achieve the goal of size reduction and customer satisfaction, a framework with two parts is described in this section. One part aims to reduce the size of VOCs, which are the source of an HOQ. The other part works toward selecting several ECs while satisfying customer expectations to an acceptable extent. Constraints not only from the nature of an HOQ, but also from budget concerns, are bound to be taken into consideration. Operations research technique is applied, and an optimal HOQ with a smaller size can then be achieved.

The procedure to reduce the size of engineering characteristics is presented in Figure 9.9.

Size reduction of VOCs. Generally, any number of customer requirements can be obtained from a marketing survey. It is normally the case that not all of them are very informative, as some of them are either duplicates or already satisfied. On the other hand, some VOCs may be very trivial, if only one or two customers out of hundreds, mentioned them. Deleting these VOCs or transferring them to another matrix for later consideration should be reasonable and acceptable in this situation. Furthermore, items considered unimportant by most customers can also be deleted if the number of VOCs is too large. This is not recommended in common conditions, for it might be risky if not done well.

If the remaining number of VOCs is still very large, categorizing them into several groups can be another solution. The manner of grouping can be determined by the decision makers in the company based on quality experience.

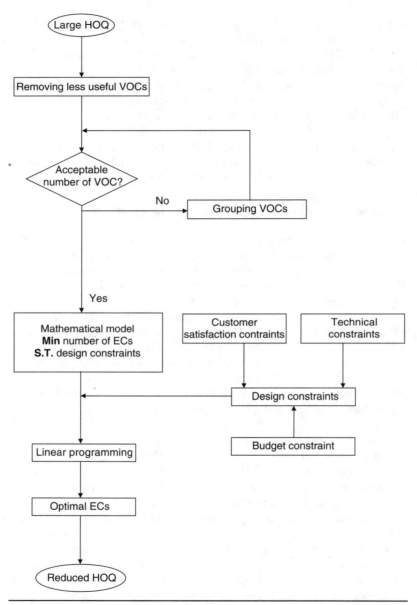

Figure 9.9 A framework for size reduction in QFD.

Every group of VOCs can then be used for a separate HOQ. A series of smaller HOQs can thus be analyzed separately. Finally, repetitive, unnecessary, and unimportant items can be removed from the original large HOQ at this stage.

Size reduction of ECs by satisfying a certain degree of customer requirements. In order to achieve the goal of eliminating some of the engineering characteristics, integer-programming techniques can be applied, with customer satisfaction levels regarded as constraints of the model. Other design constraints include technical constraints, which are reflected in the roof matrix, and budget constraints, as resources for quality improvement are always limited. A mathematical model is formulated in the following.

A Mathematical Model for Size Reduction of ECs

Before the development of our model, relationships should be normalized to obtain more meaningful descriptions of the relationships between VOCs and ECs. Traditionally, a weight of 9 is used for strong relationships, 3 is used for moderate relationships and 1 for weak relationships. Lyman (1990) recommended a normalization transform on the relationship values to generate more meaningful representations of the design priorities. An extension of Lyman's normalization procedure that can accommodate dependencies was then developed by Wasserman (1993). Several other techniques were also applied to normalize the relationships in a HOQ. Islam and Liu (1995), for example, used AHP to do the normalization. Each methodology has its own advantages and shortcomings, but all of them can lead the decision maker on the way toward a better interpretation of the relationship matrix in HOQ. The normalization is especially useful when quantitative analysis is needed.

The AHP method is used in this study to normalize the relationships by pair-wise comparisons among the three relationships. The normalized relationships are shown in Table 9.3.

The normalized relationship, R_{ij}^{norm}, is interpreted as the change in the fulfillment level of the ith VOC, as the jth EC is fulfilled to a level of 1.

In order to make the best use of limited resources, we make the assumption that all the engineering characteristics can be completely fulfilled and are completely fulfilled if included in the reduced HOQ. X_j is thus defined to be 1 if the jth item is selected to be included in the reduced HOQ, indicating that it is fully fulfilled to meet customer requirements. Otherwise, it is 0 denoting that it has been abandoned during the size reduction process. Thus, $X_j = 1$ if the jth engineering characteristic is included in the reduced HOQ; 0 if it is abandoned.

Table 9.3   The normalized relationships using AHP.

	Strong	Medium	Weak	Normalized relationship
Strong	1	3	9	0:69
Medium	1/3	1	3	0.23
Weak	1/9	1/3	1	0.08

The objective is then to reduce the number of engineering characteristics selected in the reduced HOQ, which is

$$\text{Min} \sum_j X_j \qquad (9.3)$$

As stated earlier, the constraints for this objective function include customer satisfaction constraints, technical constraints, and budget constraints. The final solution can be obtained by considering all of the constraints.

Customer Satisfaction Constraints

In order to catch up with the rapid pace of pushing forward high quality products to the world market, new product can be designed by satisfying customers to a high level, but not 100 percent. This will accelerate the production cycle, and at the same time offer a quick response to customer requirements. This will also ensure the satisfaction of customers, for customers are normally satisfied when their requirements are fulfilled to an acceptable degree. According to Colton and Staples (1997), customers are supposed to be satisfied if the customer requirements can be fulfilled to a reasonable level.

Suppose SL_i is the satisfaction level required by customers for the ith VOC and R_{ij}^{norm} are the normalized relationships. Then, the satisfaction level constraint for each of the VOC item is

$$\sum_j R_{ij}^{norm} X_j \geq SL_i \qquad (9.4)$$

On the other hand, if the customers require an overall satisfaction level instead of requiring a satisfaction level for each item, it can be expressed as

$$\sum_i W_i \sum_j R_{ij}^{norm} X_j \geq SL \qquad (9.5)$$

where W_i is the relative importance of the ith VOC and SL is the overall satisfaction level.

Technical Constraints

The correlation matrix in the roof of the HOQ is a very important part of the QFD analysis. Several researchers have attempted to include the roof matrix in the quantitative analysis of QFD. In 1995, Islam and Liu (1995) tried to add consideration of the roof matrix to their optimization model. Kim (1997) further suggested two types of constraints representing the associations among the engineering characteristics. In this study, we propose that the roof matrix can in fact be used as technical constraints, and thus should be seriously considered when a certain level of customer satisfaction is to be ensured during the size reduction process.

Generally, there are two kinds of correlation between engineering characteristics, namely, negative and positive correlation. In order to meet the purpose of eliminating some of the engineering characteristics to reduce the size of the HOQ, negative correlation should be given serious consideration. The two engineering characteristics with negative correlation can be reasonably regarded as not being able to be completely fulfilled at the same time. Fulfillment of one of them will give a negative effect to the fulfillment of the other. This leads to the avoidance of including the two items in the reduced HOQ at the same time. On the other hand, from a technical point of view, one should avoid including both of the engineering characteristics in the reduced HOQ, for it is a waste of resources if one fulfillment will decrease another. It will also raise technical difficulty for the engineers.

Thus, the technical constraints are

$$X_s + X_k \le 1 \qquad (9.6)$$

if the sth engineering characteristic has a negative correlation with the kth engineering characteristic, which means the two cannot both be selected in the reduced HOQ.

It should be noted that if special situations occur, such as the two ECs each being extremely important for the product quality, or the negative relationship between the two ECs not being very strong, the decision makers can still include both items in the reduced HOQ. The above technical constraints, in this situation, can be removed from the design constraints of the optimization model.

Budget Constraints

When trying to improve the quality of products to maximize customer satisfaction, resources are always limited, as most of the quality improvement projects have certain budget constraints. Hence, the total amount of financial resources used to fulfill the engineering characteristics should not exceed this budget.

Suppose c_j is the cost associated with complete fulfillment of the jth engineering characteristic. Then

$$\sum_j c_j X_j \leq B \tag{9.7}$$

where B is the budget for quality improvement.

A Model for Size Reduction in HOQ

The overall model is then

$$\text{Min} \sum_j X_j$$

subject to

(1) $\sum_j R_{ij}^{norm} X_j \geq SL_i$ or $\sum_i W_i \sum_j R_{ij}^{norm} X_j \geq SL$

*(2) $X_s + X_k \leq 1$ if there is negative correlation between these two items

(3) $\sum_j c_j X_j \leq B$

(4) $X_j = 1$ if it is included in the reduced HOQ and 0 otherwise
      $j = 1, 2, \ldots n$ if there are n items of engineering characteristics
      in the original HOQ.

By using this model, the number of the engineering characteristics will be reduced by satisfying a reasonable degree of customer requirements, and selecting only a few of the engineering characteristics to achieve this objective.

An Illustrative Example

The tourist camp stove designed by a fictitious company named Backpacking (Thurston and Locascio, 1993) is used here again as a simple illustrative example for size reduction (see Figure 9.10).

---

* Constraints can be ignored if both of the engineering characteristics are specially needed in the quality improvement.

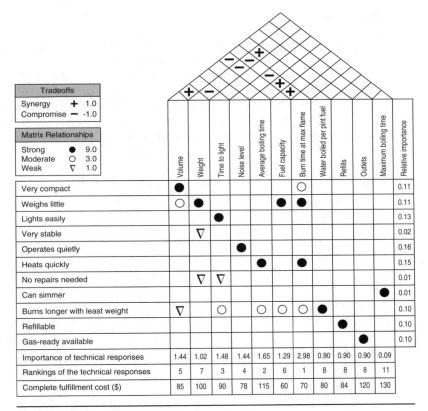

Figure 9.10 The HOQ with cost elements.

Size Reduction of VOCs

After careful consideration, "Can simmer" is removed from the list of VOCs because it is already satisfied. On the other hand, "No repairs needed" is relatively unimportant (0.01) and only has weak relationships with the ECs. Reliability analysis could be applied later to achieve this customer expectation. Thus, this item can be ignored here. Furthermore, "Very stable" with its importance of 0.02 can also be removed from the original HOQ. Thus, three items of VOCs can be removed from the HOQ through size reduction in this stage. The remaining HOQ will have eight VOCs.

Size Reduction of ECs

Since "Can simmer" was already deleted from the VOCs above, the last engineering characteristic, "Maximum boiling time," can then be deleted from the ECs, for its only relationship is with the VOC of "Can simmer."

Suppose the acceptable satisfaction level for each of the VOCs is 60 percent, and the cost associated with the complete fulfillment for the ECs are those shown in the last row of Figure 9.10. The budget for the quality improvement, on the other hand, is supposed to be \$1,000. After the normalized relationships is used, the optimization model becomes,

Minimize $X_1 + X_2 + X_3 + X_4 + X_5 + X_6 + X_7 + X_8 + X_9 + X_{10}$

Subject to:

1. *Customer satisfaction constraints*

$0.69X_1 + 0.23X_7 \geq 60\%$
$0.23X_1 + 0.69X_2 + 0.69X_6 + 0.69X_7 \geq 60\%$
$0.69X_3 \geq 60\%$
$0.69X_4 \geq 60\%$
$0.69X_5 + 0.69X_7\ 60\%$
$0.08X_1 + 0.23X_3 + 0.23X_5 + 0.23X_6 + 0.23X_7 + 0.69X_8 \geq 60\%$
$0.69X_9 \geq 60\%$
$0.69X_{10} \geq 60\%$

2. *Technical constraints*

$X_1 + X_6 \leq 1; X_2 + X_3 \leq 1; X_2 + X_6 \leq 1; X_2 + X_7 \leq 1; X_4 + X_7 \leq 1$

3. *Cost constraints*

$85X_1 + 100X_2 + 90X_3 + 78X_4 + 115X_5 + 60X_6 + 70X_7 + 80X_8 + 84X_9 + 120X_{10} \leq 1000$
and $X_j = 0$ or 1.

However, the calculation process showed that there is no solution for this model. After investigation, X_4 and X_7 are technically allowed to stay together. Thus the last technical constraint ($X_4 + X_7 \leq 1$) is ignored, and an optimal solution is then obtained. After that, another three items of ECs (X_2, X_6 and X_8) can be removed from the HOQ and the remaining HOQ has only seven ECs instead of eleven. The reduced HOQ is then shown as Figure 9.11, which is about half the size of the original HOQ. This can be analyzed with other advanced methods and the results will not be much different from the analysis of the original but much larger, HOQ.

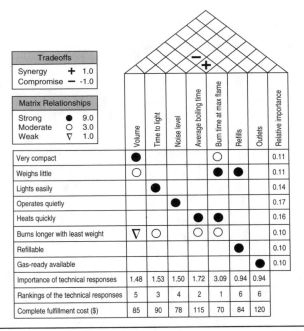

Figure 9.11 The reduced HOQ.

Glossary

Analysis of variance (ANOVA)—A statistical procedure studying the amount of variation in a process to determine if a factor is significant or the variation is caused by random noise.

Analytic hierarchy process (AHP)—A multicriteria decision-making technique particularly useful for evaluating complex multiattribute alternatives involving subjective and intangible criteria.

Benchmarking—An approach to identifying the best practice in another organizational unit, followed by its analysis and adoption.

Brainstorming—A technique for problem solving that involves the spontaneous generation of as wide a spectrum of ideas as possible.

Center of gravity—The center of gravity (or centroid) of a distribution is obtained by computing the first moment of the distribution.

Competitive assessments—The customer's opinion of the competing products is assessed for their ability to satisfy each customer requirement.

Confidence interval—A statistically estimated range of values that is likely to include the true value.

Conjoint analysis—A statistical technique used in the analysis of subjective questionnaire responses and a versatile marketing research technique that can provide valuable information for market segmentation, new product development, forecasting, and pricing decisions.

Consistency ratio—An index used to indicate the degree of inconsistency of judgments in a decision matrix in AHP analysis.

Correlation matrix—The triangular matrix at the top of the HOQ that indicates the interactions between different design requirements.

Correspondence analysis—A perceptual mapping technique that is based on data where respondents are asked to identify only the attributes that relate to (or correspond with) the subject of the study.

Crisp number—Precise or discrete values used in fuzzy analysis, as opposed to a fuzzy number, which represents a range of possible values.

Cross-functional team—A cross-organizational team of experts representing relevant units, including R&D, design, production, human resources, finance, marketing, sales, and so on.

Defuzzification—The process of transforming a fuzzy output of a fuzzy inference system into a crisp output.

Design of experiments—A statistical method dealing with planning, conducting, analyzing, and interpreting controlled tests to evaluate the factors that control the value of a parameter or group of parameters.

Exponential smoothing—A method of forecasting that bases the forecast on a weighted average of current and past values.

Factor analysis—A type of analysis that takes a large number of variables and aims to identify a small number of factors that explain the interrelations among the variables.

Failure mode and effect analysis—A bottom-up procedure used in understanding the problems, errors, and failures in a system or process.

Future voice of the customer—The future wants and desires of the customer, either expressed or predicted.

Fuzzification—The process of generating membership values for a fuzzy variable using membership functions.

Fuzzy set theory—A method to deal with uncertainty in the definition of objects or phenomena; uses definitions with variable amounts of "vagueness."

House of quality (HOQ)—A type of conceptual map that provides a means for interfunctional planning and communication.

Kano model—A model that classifies product attributes, based on how they are perceived by customers and their effect on customer satisfaction, ranging from "disgust," through neutrality, to "delight."

Lead user—Existing or potential customers who can contribute to identification of future opportunities and evaluation of emerging concepts or new products.

Membership function—A function used in fuzzy analysis that specifies the degree to which a given input belongs to a set or is related to a concept.

Planning matrix—A matrix used in the HOQ that contains strategic marketing information and planning decisions, such as customer satisfaction benchmarking and sales point.

Quality function deployment (QFD)—A structured method of deploying the attributes of a product or service desired by the customer throughout all the appropriate functional components of an organization.

Relationship matrix—The main matrix in HOQ that indicates the strength of the relationship between the customer requirements and the technical requirements.

SERVQUAL model—A system for service quality measurement that focuses on service gaps that affect service quality.

Sensitivity analysis—The study on how small changes in the independent variable affect the dependent variable.

Total quality management—A management philosophy and company practices that aim to harness the human and material resources of an organization in the most effective way to achieve the objectives of the organization.

Triangular fuzzy number (TFN)—A special type of fuzzy membership function that is of a triangular shape.

Tukey's method—A statistical comparison procedure for making pair-wise comparisons among means.

Variability analysis—The study of the effect on the results of interest caused by the expected variability of input variables.

Voice of the customer (VOC)—A term to describe the stated and unstated customer needs or requirements that should be the starting point of any quality analysis.

References

Abdul-Rahman, H., C. L. Kwan, and P. C. Woods, (1999), Quality function deployment in construction design: Application in low-cost housing design, *International Journal of Quality & Reliability Management,* 16, 591–605.

Adiano, C. and A. V. Roth (1994), Beyond the house of quality: Dynamic QFD, *Benchmarking for Quality Management & Technology,* 1, 25–37.

Akao, Y. (1990), *Quality function deployment: Integrating customer requirements into product design,* Cambridge, MA: Productivity Press.

Akao, Y. and G. H. Mazur (2003), The leading edge in QFD: Past, present and future, *International Journal of Quality & Reliability Management,* 20, 20–35.

Armacost, R. L., P. J. Componation, M. A. Mullens, and W. W. Swart (1994), AHP framework for prioritizing customer requirements in QFD: An industrialized housing application, *IIE Transactions,* 26, 72–79.

Bahrami, A. (1994), Routine design with information content and fuzzy quality function deployment, *Journal of Intelligent Manufacturing,* 5, 203–210.

Balthazard, P. A. and V. B. Gargeya (1995), Reinforcing QFD with group support systems: Computer-supported collaboration for quality in design, *International Journal of Quality & Reliability Management,* 12, 43–62.

Barnett, W. D. and M. K. Raja (1995), Application of QFD to the software development process, *International Journal of Quality & Reliability Management,* 12, 24–42.

Bech, A. C., M. Hansen, and L. Wienberg (1997), Application of house of quality in translation of consumer needs into sensory attributes measurable by descriptive sensory analysis, *Food Quality & Preference,* 8, 329–348.

Belhe, U. and A. Kusiak (1996), The house of quality in a design process, *International Journal of Production Research,* 34, 2119–2131.

Bergman, B. and B. Klefsjo (1994), *Quality: From customer needs to customer satisfaction,* London, New York: McGraw-Hill.

Berry, L. L., A. Parasuraman, and V. A. Zeithaml (1994), Improving service quality in America: Lessons learned, *Academy of Management Executive,* 8(2), 32–52.

Bier, I. D. and R. Cornesky (2001), Using QFD to construct a higher education curriculum, *Quality Progress,* 34, 64–68.

Bird, S. (1992), Object-oriented expert system architectures for manufacturing quality management, *Journal of Manufacturing Systems,* 11, 50–60.

Burke. E., J. M. Kloeber, Jr., and R. F. Deckro (2003), Using and abusing QFD scores, *Quality Engineering,* 15, 9–21.

Burn, G. R. (1994), Quality function deployment. In *Managing quality,* edited by B. G. Dale and J. J. Plunkett, London: Philip Allan.

Burrows, P. (1991), In search of the perfect product, *Electronic Business,* 17, 70–74.

Camp, R. C. (1989), *Benchmarking: The search for industry best practices that lead to superior performance,* Milwaukee, WI: ASQC Quality Press.

Carman, J. M. (1990), Consumer perceptions of service quality: An assessment of the SERVQUAL dimensions, *Journal of Retailing,* 66, 33–35.

Chan, L. K., H. P. Kao, A. Ng, and M. L. Wu (1999), Rating the importance of customer needs in quality function deployment by fuzzy and entropy methods, *International Journal of Production Research,* 37, 2499–2518.

Chan, L. K. and M. L. Wu (1998), Prioritizing the technical measures in quality function deployment, *Quality Engineering,* 10, 467–479.

Chan, L. K. and M. L. Wu (2002), Quality function deployment: A literature review, *European Journal of Operational Research,* 143, 463–497.

Chan, L. K. and M. L. Wu (2003), Quality function deployment: A comprehensive review of its concepts and methods, *Quality Engineering,* 15, 23–35.

Charteris, W. (1993), Quality function deployment—A quality engineering technology for the food-industry, *Journal of Social Dairy Technology,* 46, 12–21.

Chen, C. L. and S. F. Bullington (1993), Development of a strategic research plan for an academic department through the use of quality function deployment, *Computers and Industrial Engineering,* 25, 49–52.

Cohen, L. (1995), *Quality function deployment: How to make QFD work for you,* Reading, MA: Addison-Wesley.

Colton, J. S. and J. W. Staples (1997), Resource allocation using QFD and softness concepts during preliminary design, *Engineering Optimization,* 28, 33–62.

Costa, A. I. A., M. Dekker, and W. M. F. Jongen (2000), Quality function deployment in the food industry: A review, *Trends in Food Science & Technology,* 11, 306–314.

Cristiano, J. J., J. K. Liker, and C. C. White, III, (2000), Customer-driven product development through quality function deployment in the U.S. and Japan, *Journal of Product Innovation Management,* 17, 286–308.

Crosby, P. (1979), *Quality is free.* New York: McGraw-Hill.

Crossfield, R. T. and B. G. Dale (1991), The use of expert systems in total quality management: An exploratory study, *Quality and Reliability Engineering International,* 7, 19–26.

CQM (1993), A special issue on Kano's methods for understanding customer-defined quality, *The Center for Quality Management Journal,* 2, 3–35.

Curry, A. and D. Herbert (1998), Continuous improvement in public services—A way forward, *Managing Service Quality,* 8, 339–349.

Czuchry, A. J., M. M. Yasin, and J. J. Dorsch (1995), A review of benchmarking literature—A proposed model for implementation, *International Journal of Materials & Product Technology,* 10, 27–45.

Day, R. G. (1993), *Quality function deployment: Linking a company with its customers,* Milwaukee, WI: ASQC Quality Press.

Delano G., G. S. Parnell, C. Smith, and M. Vance (2000), Quality function deployment and decision analysis—A R&D case study, *International Journal of Operations and Production Management,* 20, 591–609.

Deming, W. E. (1993), *The new economics for industry, government, education,* Cambridge, MA: MIT Center for Advanced Engineering Study.

Denton, D. K. (1990), The service imperative, *Personnel Journal,* 69, 66–74.

De Vera, D., T. Glennon, A. A. Kenny, M. A. H. Khan, and M. Mayer (1988), An automotive case study, *Quality Progress,* 21, 35–38.

Dika, R. J. (1995), QFD implementation at Chrysler: The first seven years. In *Quality up, costs down: A manager's guide to Taguchi methods and QFD,* edited by W. E. Eureka, N. E. Ryan, Dearborn, MI: ASI Press, pp. 123–163.

Doukas, L., W. Parkins, and C. Jeyaratnam (1995), Integrating quality factors into system design, *Proceedings of the Annual IEEE International Engineering Management Conference,* Piscataway, NJ, pp. 235–240.

Dube, L., M. D. Johnson, and L. M. Renaghan (1999), Adapting the QFD approach to extended service transactions, *Production & Operations Management,* 8, 301–317.

Elboushi, M. I. and J. S. Sherif (1997), Object-oriented software design utilizing quality function deployment, *Journal of Systems & Software,* 38, 133–143.

Erikkson, I. and F. McFadden (1993), Quality function deployment: A tool to improve software quality, *Information & Software Technology,* 35, 491–498.

Ermer, D. S. (1995), Using QFD becomes an educational experience for students and faculty, *Quality Progress,* 28, 131–136.

Ermer, D. S. and M. K. Kniper (1998), Delighting the customer: Quality function deployment for quality service design, *Total Quality Management,* 9, S86–S91.

Eureka, W. E. and N. E. Ryan (1994), *The Customer-driven Company: Managerial Perspectives on Quality Function Deployment,* Dearborn, MI: ASI Press.

Foster, W. F. (2001), Customer driven healthcare: QFD for process improvement and cost reduction, *Quality Progress,* 34, 123–124.

Franceschini, F. and S. Rossetto (1995), QFD: The problem of comparing technical/engineering design requirements, *Research in Engineering Design,* 7, 270–78.

Franceschini, F. and S. Rossetto (1997), Design for quality: Selecting a product's technical features, *Quality Engineering,* 9, 681–688.

Franceschini, F. and S. Rossetto (1998), Quality function deployment: How to improve its use, *Total Quality Management,* 9, 491–500.

Franceschini, F. and M. Terzago (1998), An application of quality function deployment to industrial training courses, *International Journal of Quality & Reliability Management,* 15, 753–768.

Franceschini, F. and M. Zappulli (1998), Product's technical quality profile design based on competition analysis and customer requirements: An application to a real case, *International Journal of Quality & Reliability Management*, 15, 431–442.

Fung, R. Y. K., K. Popplewell, and J. Xie (1998), An intelligent hybrid system for customer requirements analysis and product attribute targets determination, *International Journal of Production Research*, 36, 13–34.

Fung, R. Y. K., J. Tang, Y. Tu, and D. Wang (2002), Product design resources optimization using a non-linear fuzzy quality function deployment model, *International Journal of Production Research*, 40, 585–599.

Ghobadian, A. and A. J. Terry (1995), How Alitalia improves service quality through quality function deployment, *Managing Service Quality*, 5, 25–30.

GOAL/QPC (1991), *Benchmarking*, GOAL/QPC Research Committee, Research Report No. 91-01, Methuen, MA: GOAL/QPC.

Goetsch, D. L. and S. B. Davis (1997), *Introduction to total quality*, 2nd ed., Upper Saddle River, NJ: Prentice Hall.

Goh, T. N., M. Xie, and W. Xie (1995), Prioritising processes in initial implementation of statistical process control, *IEEE Transactions on Engineering Management*, 45, 247–353.

Govers, C.P.M. (2001), QFD not just a tool but a way of quality management. *International Journal of Production Economy*, 69, 151–159.

Graessel, B. and P. Zeidler (1993), Using quality function deployment to improve customer service, *Quality Progress*, 26 (11), 59–63.

Griffin, A. (1991), Evaluating development processes: QFD as an example, Working Paper, Report No. 91–121, Cambridge, MA: Marketing Science Institute.

Griffin, A. (1992), Evaluating QFD's use in US firms as a process for developing products, *Journal of Product Innovation Management*, 9, 171–187.

Griffin, A. and J. R. Hauser (1993), The voice of the customer, *Marketing Science*, 12, 1–27.

Guiffrida, A. L. and R. Nagi (1998), Fuzzy set theory applications in production management research: A literature survey, *Journal of Intelligent Manufacturing*, 9, 39–56.

Gustafsson, A., F. Ekdahl, and B. Bergman (1999), Conjoint analysis: A useful tool in the design process, *Total Quality Management*, 10, 327–343.

Haag, S., M. K. Raja, and L. L. Schkade (1996), Quality function deployment usage in software development, *Communications of the ACM*, 39, 41–49.

Hair, J. F., Jr., R. E. Anderson, R. L. Tatham, and W. C. Black (1998), *Multivariate data analysis*, 5th ed., Upper Saddle River, NJ: Prentice Hall.

Han, C. H., J. K. Kim, S. H. Choi, and S. H. Kim (1998), Determination of information system development priority: Using quality function deployment, *Computers and Industrial Engineering*, 35, 241–244.

Hanke, J. E. and A. G. Reitsch (1998), *Business forecasting*, 6th ed., Upper Saddle River, NJ: Prentice Hall.

Hauser, J. R. (1993), How Puritan-Bennett used the house of quality, *Sloan Management Review*, 34, 61–70.

Hauser, J. R. and D. Clausing (1988), The house of quality, *Harvard Business Review,* 66(3), 63–73.

Hepworth, M. (1997), How to stem revenue loss resulting from customer dissatisfaction, *CMA Magazine,* 71, 31.

Herzwurm, G. and S. Schockert (2003), The leading edge in QFD for software and electronic business, *International Journal of Quality & Reliability Management,* 20, 36–55.

Huang, G. Q. and K. L. Mak (2002), Synchronous quality function deployment (QFD) over World Wide Web, *Computers and Industrial Engineering,* 42, 425–431.

Hunter, M. R. and R. D. V. Landingham (1994), Listening to the customer using QFD, *Quality Progress,* 27, 55–59.

Hutton, D. (2001), Quality Function Deployment (QFD), From *http://www.dhutton.com/visitors/articles/artqfd.html.*

Hwarng, H. B. and C. Teo (2001), Translating customers' voices into operations requirements—A QFD application in higher education, *International Journal of Quality & Reliability Management,* 18, 195–225.

Islam, A. and M. C. Liu (1995), Determination of design parameters using QFD, *Transactions from the 7th Symposium on Quality Function Deployment,* Ann Arbor, Mich. : QFD Institute, pp. 61–74.

Jackson, A. E., R. R. Safford, and W. W. Swart (1994), Roadmap to current benchmarking literature, *Journal of Management in Engineering,* 10, 60–67.

Jeong, M. and H. Oh (1998), Quality function deployment: An extended framework for service quality and customer satisfaction in the hospitality industry, *International Journal of Hospitality Management,* 17, 375–390.

Kano, N., N. Seraku, F. Takahashi, and S. Tsuji (1984), Attractive quality and must-be quality, *Hinshitsu* (Quality, The Journal of Japanese Society for Quality Control), 14, 39–48.

Karlsson, J. (1997), Managing software requirements using quality function deployment, *Software Quality Journal,* 6, 311–325.

Karsak, E. E., S. Sozer, and S. E. Alptekin (2003), Product planning in quality function deployment using a combined analytic network process and goal programming approach, *Computers & Industrial Engineering,* 44, 171–190.

Kathawala, Y. and J. Motwani (1994), Implementing quality function deployment: A system approach, *TQM Magazine,* 6, 31–37.

Kaufmann, A. and M. M. Gupta (1985), *Introduction to fuzzy arithmetic: Theory and applications,* New York: Van Nostrand Reinhold.

Kenny, A. A. (1988), A new paradigm for quality assurance, *Quality Progress,* 21, 30–32.

Khoo, L. P. and N. C. Ho (1996), Framework of a fuzzy quality function deployment system, *International Journal of Production Research,* 34, 299–311.

Kim, J. K., C. H. Han, S. H. Choi, and S. H. Kim (1998), A knowledge-based approach to the quality function deployment, *Computers & Industrial Engineering,* 35, 233–236.

Kim, K. J. (1997), Determining optimal design characteristic levels in quality function deployment, *Quality Engineering,* 10, 295–307.

Kim, K. J., H. Moskowitz, A. Dhingra, and G. Evans (2000), Fuzzy multicriteria models for quality function deployment, *European Journal of Operational Research,* 121, 504–518.

Kim, K. J., J. S. Shin, and H. Moskowitz (1997), Design decomposition in quality function deployment. In *Essays in decision making: A volume in honour of Stanley Zionts,* edited by M. H. Karwan, J. Spronk, and J. Wallenius, Berlin: Springer Verlag.

King, R. (1995), Designing Products and Services That Customers Want. Portland: Productivity Press.

Kuei, C.H. and M.H. Lu (1997), An integrated approach to service quality improvement, *International Journal of Quality Science,* 2, 24–36.

Kwong, C. K. and H. Bai (2002), A fuzzy AHP approach to the determination of importance weights of customer requirements in quality function deployment, *Journal of Intelligent Manufacturing,* 13, 367–377.

LaBahn, D. W., A. Ali, and R. Krapfel (1996), New product development cycle time—The influence of project and process factors in small manufacturing companies, *Journal of Business Research,* 36, 179–188.

Lai, Y. J. and C. L. Hwang (1994), *Fuzzy multiple objective decision making methods and applications,* Berlin: Springer-Verlag.

Lam, K. and X. Zhao (1998), An application of quality function deployment to improve the quality of teaching, *International Journal of Quality & Reliability Management,* 15, 389–413.

Langley, G. J., K. M. Nolan, T. W. Nolan, C. L. Norman, and L. P. Provost (1996), *The improvement guide: A practical approach to enhancing organizational performance,* San Francisco: Jossey-Bass Publishers.

Lee, S. F., K. K. Lo, R. F. Leung, and A. O. K. Sai (2000), Strategy formulation framework for vocational education: Integrating SWOT analysis, Balanced Scorecard, QFD methodology and MBNA education criteria, *Managerial Auditing Journal,* 15(8), 407–423.

Liner, M., E. N. Loredo, H. S. Gitlow, and N. G. Einspruch (1997), Quality function deployment applied to electronic component design, *Quality Engineering,* 9, 237–248.

Liu, X. F. and J. Yen (1996), An analytic framework for specifying and analyzing imprecise requirements, *Proceedings of the 18th International Conference on Software Engineering,* Los Alamitos, Calif. : IEEE Computer Society Press, pp. 60–69

Locascio, A. and D. L. Thurston (1998), Transforming the house of quality to a multiobjective optimization formulation, *Structural Optimization,* 16, 136–146.

Lu, M. H. and C. H. Kuei (1995), Strategic marketing planning: A quality function deployment approach, *International Journal of Quality & Reliability Management,* 12, 85–96.

Lu, M. H., C. N. Madu, C. H. Kuei, and D. Winokur (1994), Integrating QFD, AHP and benchmarking in strategic marketing, *Journal of Business & Industrial Marketing,* 9, 41–50.

Lyman, D. (1990), Deployment normalization, *Transactions from the 2nd Symposium on Quality Function Deployment,* Ann Arbor, Mich. : QFD Institute, pp. 307–315.

Maier, M. W. (1995), Quantitative engineering analysis with QFD, *Quality Engineering,* 7, 733–746.

Mallon, J. C. and D. E. Mulligan (1993), Quality function deployment—A system for meeting customers' needs, *Journal of Construction Engineering & Management-ASCE,* 119, 516–531.

Masud, A. S. M. and E. B. Dean (1993), Using fuzzy sets in quality function deployment, *Proceedings of the 2nd Industrial Engineering Research Conference,* Los Angeles, CA, pp. 270–274.

Masui, K., T. Sakao, M. Kobayashi, and A. Inaba (2003), Applying quality function deployment to environmentally conscious design, *International Journal of Quality & Reliability Management,* 20, 90–106.

Matzler, K. and H. H. Hinterhuber (1998), How to make product development projects more successful by integrating Kano's model of customer satisfaction into quality function deployment, *Technovation,* 18, 25–38.

McLaurin, D. L. and S. Bell (1993), Making customer service more than just a slogan, *Quality Progress,* 26, 35–39.

Mendenhall, W. and T. Sincich (1995), *Statistics for engineering and the sciences,* Englewood Cliffs, NJ: Prentice Hall.

Mizuno, S. and Y. Akao (1994), QFD: *The customer-driven approach to quality planning and deployment,* Tokyo: Asian Productivity Organization.

Mohr-Hackson, I. (1996), Quality function deployment: A valuable marketing tool, *Journal of Marketing Theory & Practice,* 4, 60–67.

Moskowitz, H. and K. J., Kim (1997), QFD optimizer: A novice friendly quality function deployment decision making support system for optimizing product designs, *Computers & Industrial Engineering,* 32, 641–655.

O'Neal, C. R. and W. C. LaFief (1992), Marketing's lead role in total quality, *Industrial Marketing Management,* 21, 133–143.

Pai, W. C. (2002), A quality-enhancing software function deployment model, *Information Systems and Management,* 19, 20–24.

Parasuraman, A., V. A. Zeithaml, and L. L. Berry (1985), A conceptual model of service quality and its implications for future research, *Journal of Marketing,* 19, 41–55.

Park, T. and K. J. Kim (1998), Determination of an optimal set of design requirements using house of quality, *Journal of Operations Management,* 16, 569–581.

Pawitra, T. A., K. C. Tan and M. Xie (1997), An application of QFD to tourist attractions in Singapore, *Proceedings from the 3rd Annual International QFD Symposium,* vol.2, Linkoping, Sweden, pp.175–188.

Pitman, G., J. Motwani, A. Kumar, and C. H. Cheng (1995), QFD application in an educational setting: A pilot field study, *International Journal of Quality & Reliability Management,* 12, 63–72.

Poh, K. H. (1998), A study of the selection of factors for DOE planning, Academic Exercise, Faculty of Engineering, National University of Singapore.

Prasad, B. (1998), Review of QFD and related deployment techniques, *Journal of Manufacturing Systems,* 17, 221–234.

Price, R. C. (1995), TQM in the R&D function, *Quality Progress,* 28, 109–111.

Pullman, M. E., W. L. Moore, and D. G. Wardell (2002), A comparison of quality function deployment and conjoint analysis in new product design, *Journal of Production & Innovation Management,* 19, 354–364.

Pun, K. F., K. S. Chin, and H. Lau (2000), A QFD/hoshin approach for service quality deployment: A case study, *Managing Service Quality,* 10, 156–170.

Punj, G. and D. W. Stewart (1983), Cluster analysis in marketing research: Review and suggestions for application, *Journal of Marketing Research,* 20, 134–148.

Radharamanan, R and L. P. Godoy (1996), Quality function deployment as applied to a health care system, *Computers & Industrial Engineering,* 31, 443–446.

Rao, C. P. and M. M. Kelkar (1997), Relative impact of performance and importance ratings on measurement of service quality, *Journal of Professional Services Marketing,* 15(2), 69–86.

Raynor, M. E. (1994), The ABCs of QFD: Formalizing the quest for cost-effective customer delight, *National Productivity Review,* 13, 351–357.

Reich, Y. (1996), AI-supported quality function deployment. In: Ein-Dor, P. (ed.), *Artificial Intelligence in Economics and Management,* Kluwer, pp 91–106.

ReVelle, J. B., J. W. Moran, and C. A. Cox (1997), *The QFD handbook,* New York: John Wiley & Sons.

Robertshaw, W. (1995), Using an objective sales point measure to incorporate elements of the Kano model into QFD, *Transactions from the 7th Symposium on Quality Function Deployment,* Ann Arbor, Mich. : QFD Institute, pp. 201–216.

Runkler, T. A. (1997), Selection of appropriate defuzzification methods using application specific properties, *IEEE Transactions on Fuzzy Systems,* 5, 72–79.

Rust, R. T. and R. L. Oliver (1994), *Service quality: New directions in theory and practice,* Thousand Oaks, California: Sage Publications.

Saaty, T. L. (1980), *The analytic hierarchy process: Planning, priority setting, resource allocation,* New York: McGraw-Hill.

Saaty, T. L. (1982), *Decision making for leaders,* Belmont, CA: Wadsworth Publishing.

Samli, A. C. (1996), Developing futuristic product portfolios: A major panacea for the sluggish American industry, *Industrial Marketing Management,* 25, 589–600.

Samson, D. and J. Wacker (1998), Maximising the 'benefits per dollar' to customers: A new organisational focus, *International Journal of Production Economics,* 54, 215–230.

Selen, W. J. and J. Schepers (2001), Design of quality service systems in the public sector: Use of quality function deployment in police services. *Total Quality Management,* 12, 677–687.

Shen, X. X. (2000), *Advancements to the house of quality in quality function deployment.* Dissertation (Ph.D.), Dept. of Industrial & Systems Engineering, Faculty of Engineering, National University of Singapore.

Shen, X. X., K. C. Tan, and M. Xie (2000), An integrated approach to innovative product development using Kano's model and QFD, *European Journal of Innovation Management,* 3, 91–99.

Shen, X. X., K. C. Tan, and M. Xie (2001), Listening to the future voice of customer using fuzzy trend analysis in QFD, *Quality Engineering,* 13, 419–426.

Shen, X. X., K. C. Tan, M. Xie, T. N. Goh, and H. Wang (1999), Sensitivity of the relationship matrix in quality function deployment, *International Journal of Industrial Engineering,* 6, 223.

Shillito, M. L. (1994), *Advanced QFD: Linking technology to market and company needs,* New York: John Wiley & Sons.

Shin, J. S. and K. J. Kim (1997), Restructuring a house of quality using factor analysis, *Quality Engineering,* 9, 739–746.

Shin, J. S., D. K. H. Fong, and K. J. Kim (1998), Complexity reduction of a house of quality chart using correspondence analysis, *Quality Management Journal,* 5, 46–58.

Sim, K. L. (2000), Analysis of house of quality in quality function development, Academic exercise, Faculty of Engineering, National University of Singapore, 2000.

Simonson, I. (1993), Get closer to your customers by understanding how they make choices, *California Management Review,* 35, 68–84.

Sivaloganathan, S. and N. F. O. Evbuomwan (1997), Quality function deployment—the technique: State of the art and future directions, *Concurrent Engineering: Research and Applications,* 5, 171–181.

Sohn, S. Y. and I. S. Choi (2001), Fuzzy QFD for supply chain management with reliability consideration, *Reliability Engineering & Systems Safety,* 72, 327–334.

Sriraman, V., P. Tosirisuk., and H. W. Chu (1990), Object-oriented databases for quality function deployment and Taguchi methods, *Computers & Industrial Engineering,* 19, 285–289.

Sullivan, L. P. (1986), Quality function deployment, *Quality Progress,* 19, 39–50.

Swanson, R. C. (1993), Quality benchmark deployment, *Quality Progress,* 26, 81–84.

Tan, C. M. and T. K. Neo (2002), QFD implementation in a discrete semiconductor industry, Proceedings 2002 Annual Reliability and Maintainability Symposium, Anaheim, LA, 484–489.

Tan, K. C., M. Xie, and E. Chia (1998), Quality function deployment and its use in designing information technology systems, *International Journal of Quality & Reliability Management,* 15, 634–645.

Taylor, S. A., A. Sharland, J. J. Cronin, and W. Bullard (1993), Recreational service quality in the international setting, *International Journal of Service Industry Management,* 4(4), 68–86.

Temponi, C., J. Yen, and W. A. Tiao (1999), House of quality: A fuzzy logic-based requirements analysis, *European Journal of Operational Research,* 117, 340–354.

Thurston, D. L. and A. Locascio (1993), Multiattribute design optimization and concurrent engineering. In *Concurrent engineering: Contemporary issues and modern design tools,* edited by H. R. Parsaei and W. G. Sullivan, Cambridge: Chapman & Hall, pp. 207–230.

Tottie, M. and T. Lager (1995), QFD—Linking the customer to the product development process as a part of the TQM concept, *R & D Management,* 25, 257–267.

Trappey, C. V., A. J. C. Trappey, and S. J. Hwang, (1996), A computerized quality function deployment approach for retail services, *Computers & Industrial Engineering,* 30, 611–622.

Tsuda, Y. (1997), Concurrent engineering case studies applying QFD models, *Concurrent Engineering: Research & Applications,* 5, 337–345.

Tukey, J. W. (1949), Comparing individual means in the analysis of variance, *Biometrics,* 5, 99–114.

Urban, G. L. and J. R. Hauser (1993), *Design and marketing of new products,* 2nd ed., Englewood Cliffs, NJ: Prentice Hall.

Vairaktarakis, G. L. (1999), Optimization tools for design and marketing of new/improved products using the house of quality, *Journal of Operations Management,* 17, 645–663.

Vaziri, H. K. (1992), Using competitive benchmarking to set goals, *Quality Progress,* 25, 81–85.

Viaene, J. and R. Januszewska (1999), Quality function deployment in the chocolate industry, *Food Quality & Preference,* 10, 377–385.

von Hippel, E. (1986), Lead users: A source of novel product concepts, *Management Science,* 32, 569–582.

Vonderembse, M. and T. S. Raghunathan (1997), Quality function deployment's impact on product development, *International Journal of Quality Science,* 2, 253–271.

Vonderembse, M., T. V Fossen., and T. S. Raghunathan (1997), Is quality function deployment good for product development? Forty companies say yes, *Quality Management Journal,* 4, 65–79.

Wang, H. (2001), *Some new approaches to IT service quality & QFD analysis.* Dissertation (Ph.D.), Dept. of Industrial & Systems Engineering, Faculty of Engineering, National University of Singapore.

Wang, H., M. Xie, and T. N. Goh (1998), A comparative study of the prioritization matrix method and the analytic hierarchy process technique in quality function deployment, *Total Quality Management,* 9, 421–430.

Wang, J. (1999), Fuzzy outranking approach to prioritize design requirements in quality function deployment, *International Journal of Production Research,* 37, 899–916.

Wasserman, G. S. (1993), On how to prioritize design requirements during the QFD planning process, *IIE Transactions,* 25, 59–65.

Wolfe, M. (1994), Development of the city of quality: A hypertext-based group decision support system for quality function deployment, *Decision Support Systems,* 11, 299–318.

Wong, A., A. M. Dean, and C. J. White (1999), Analyzing service quality in the hospitality industry, *Managing Service Quality,* 9(2), 136–143.

Xie, M., T. N. Goh, and H. Wang(1998), A study of the sensitivity of 'customer voice' in QFD analysis, *International Journal of Industrial Engineering,* 5, 301–307.

Yamashina, H., T. Ito, and H. Kawada (2002), Innovative product development process by integrating QFD and TRIZ, *International Journal of Production Research,* 40, 1031–1050.

Yoshizawa, T., Y. Akao, M. Ono, and H. Shingo (1993), Recent aspects of QFD in the Japanese software industry, *Quality Engineering,* 5, 495–504.

Zadeh, L. A. (1965), Fuzzy sets, *Information & Control,* 8, 338–353.

Zadeh, L. A. (1975), The concept of a linguistic variable and its application to approximate reasoning, *Information Sciences,* 8, 199–249.

Zairi, M. (1996), *Benchmarking for best practice: Continuous learning through sustainable innovation,* Oxford: Butterworth-Heinemann.

Zairi, M. and M. A. Youssef (1995), Quality function deployment: A main pillar for successful total quality management and product development, *International Journal of Quality & Reliability Management,* 12, 9–23.

Zeithaml, V. A., A. Parasuraman, and L. L. Berry (1990), *Delivering quality service: Balancing customer perceptions and expectations,* New York: Free Press.

Zhang, X., J. Bode, and S. Ren (1996), Neural networks in quality function deployment, *Computers & Industrial Engineering,* 31, 669–673.

Zhao, R. and R. Govind (1991), Defuzzification of fuzzy intervals, *Fuzzy Sets and Systems,* 43, 45–55.

Zultner, R. E. (1990), Software quality [function] deployment: Applying QFD to software, *Transactions from the 2nd Symposium on Quality Function Deployment,* Ann Arbor, Mich. : QFD Institute, pp.133–143.

Zultner, R. E. (1993), Priorities: The analytic hierarchy process in QFD, *Transactions from the 5th Symposium on Quality Function Deployment,* Ann Arbor, Mich. : QFD Institute, pp. 459–466.

About the Authors

M. Xie received his PhD in Quality Technology from Linkoping University, Sweden, in 1987 and has published over 100 articles in refereed journals and four books in these areas. Professor Xie is a Senior Member of ASQ, IEEE, and IIE. He serves on the editorial boards of several quality, related journals.

K. C. Tan obtained his PhD from the Department of Industrial Engineering and Operations Research at the Virginia Polytechnic Institute and State University in 1990. Professor Tan is also Associate Director of the Office of Quality Management at National University of Singapore.

T. N. Goh received his PhD from the University of Wisconsin–Madison in 1973. Currently Professor Goh is Director, Office of Quality Management, National University of Singapore. He is an elected Academician of the IAQ and a Fellow of the ASQ. He serves as an Associate Editor of Quality Engineering and is on the editorial boards of several other international research journals.

Index